THE
•LATER CAVE-MEN•

Industrial and Social History Series

By KATHARINE ELIZABETH DOPP, Ph. D.

The Extension Division of The University of Chicago. Author of "The Place of Industries in Elementary Education"

Book I. THE TREE-DWELLERS. THE AGE OF FEAR.
Illustrated with a map, 14 full-page and 46 text drawings in half-tone by HOWARD V. BROWN. Cloth. Square 12mo. 158 pages; 45 cents.
For the primary grades.

Book II. THE EARLY CAVE-MEN. THE AGE OF COMBAT.
Illustrated with a map, 17 full-page and 68 text drawings in half-tone by HOWARD V. BROWN. Cloth. Square 12mo. 183 pages; 45 cents.
For the primary grades.

Book III. THE LATER CAVE-MEN. THE AGE OF THE CHASE.
Illustrated with 27 full-page and 87 text drawings in half-tone by HOWARD V. BROWN. Cloth. Square 12mo. 197 pages; 45 cents.
For the primary grades.

Book IV. THE EARLY SEA PEOPLE. FIRST STEPS IN THE CONQUEST OF THE WATERS. Illustrated with 21 full-page and 110 text drawings in half-tone by HOWARD V. BROWN and KYOHEI INUKAI. Cloth. Square 12mo. 224 pages; 50 cents.
For the intermediate grades.

Other volumes, dealing with the early development of pastoral and agricultural life, the age of metals, travel, trade, and transportation, will follow.

"A feeling of awe came over them while they worked."—PAGE 172.

THE
LATER CAVE-MEN

KATHARINE ELIZABETH DOPP
Lecturer in Education.
In the Extension Division of the
University of Chicago

RAND McNALLY & COMPANY

CHICAGO   NEW YORK   LONDON

The Rand-McNally Press
Chicago

PREFACE

THE series, of which this is the third volume, is an attempt to meet a need that has been felt for several years by parents and physicians, as well as by teachers, supervisors, and others who are actively interested in educational and social progress. The need of practical activity, which for long ages constituted the entire education of mankind, is at last recognized by the elementary school. It has been introduced in many places and already results have been attained which demonstrate that it is possible to introduce practical activity in such a way as to afford the child a sound development — physically, intellectually, and morally — and at the same time equip him for efficient social service. The question that is perplexing educators at the present time is, therefore, not one regarding the value of practical activity, but rather one of ways and means by which practical activity can be harnessed to the educational work.

The discovery of the fact that steam is a force that can do work had to await the invention of machinery by means of which to apply the new force to industrial processes. The use of practical activity will likewise necessitate many changes in the educational machinery before its richest results are realized. Yet the conditions that attend the introduction of practical activity as a motive power in education are very different from those that attended the introduction of the use of steam. In the case of steam the problem was that of applying a new force to an old work. In the case of practical activity it is a question of restoring a factor which, from the earliest times until within the last two or three decades, has operated as a permanent educational force.

The situation that has recently deprived the child of the oppor-

tunity to participate in industrial processes is due, as is well
known, to the rapid development of our industrial system. Since
the removal of industrial processes from the home the public has
awakened to the fact that the child is being deprived of one of the
most potent educational influences, and efforts have already been
made to restore the educational factor that was in danger of being
lost. This is the significance of the educational movement at the
present time.

As long as a simple organization of society prevailed, the school
was not called upon to take up the practical work; but now society
has become so complex that the use of practical activity is abso-
lutely essential. Society to-day makes a greater demand than ever
before upon each and all of its members for special skill and knowledge, as well as for breadth of view. These demands can be met
only by such an improvement in educational facilities as corres-
ponds to the increase in the social demand. Evidently the school
must lay hold of all of the educational forces within its reach.

In the transitional movement it is not strange that new factors
are being introduced without relation to the educational process
as a whole. The isolation of manual training, sewing, and cooking
from the physical, natural, and social sciences is justifiable only
on the ground that the means of establishing more organic rela-
tions are not yet available. To continue such isolated activities
after a way is found of harnessing them to the educational work
is as foolish as to allow steam to expend itself in moving a loco-
motive up and down the tracks without regard to the destiny of
the detached train.

This series is an attempt to facilitate the transitional movement
in education which is now taking place by presenting educative
materials in a form sufficiently flexible to be readily adapted to the
needs of the school that has not yet been equipped for manual
training, as well as to the needs of the one that has long recognized
practical activity as an essential factor in its work. Since the
experience of the race in industrial and social processes embodies,

better than any other experiences of mankind, those things which at the same time appeal to the whole nature of the child and furnish him the means of interpreting the complex processes about him, this experience has been made the groundwork of the present series.

In order to gain cumulative results of value in explaining our own institutions, the materials used have been selected from the life of Aryan peoples. That we are not yet in possession of all the facts regarding the life of the early Aryans is not considered a sufficient reason for withholding from the child those facts that we have when they can be adapted to his use. Information regarding the early stages of Aryan life is meager. Enough has been established, however, to enable us to mark out the main lines of progress through the hunting, the fishing, the pastoral, and the agricultural stages, as well as to present the chief problems that confronted man in taking the first steps in the use of metals, and in the establishment of trade. Upon these lines, marked out by the geologist, the paleontologist, the archæologist, and the anthropologist, the first numbers of this series are based.

A generalized view of the main steps in the early progress of the race, which it is thus possible to present, is all that is required for educational ends. Were it possible to present the subject in detail, it would be tedious and unprofitable to all save the specialist. To select from the monotony of the ages that which is most vital, to so present it as to enable the child to participate in the process by which the race has advanced, is a work more in keeping with the spirit of the age. To this end the presentation of the subject is made: First, by means of questions, which serve to develop the habit of making use of experience in new situations; second, by narrative, which is employed merely as a literary device for rendering the subject more available to the child; and third, by suggestions for practical activities that may be carried out in hours of work or play, in such a way as to direct into useful channels energy which when left undirected is apt to express itself in trivial if not

in anti-social forms.   No part of a book is more significant to the
child than the illustrations.   In preparing the illustrations for this
series as great pains have been taken to furnish the child with
ideas that will guide him in his practical activities as to illustrate
the text itself.

Mr. Howard V. Brown, the artist who executed the drawings,
has been aided in his search for authentic originals by the late
J. W. Powell, *director of the United States Bureau of Ethnology, Wash-
ington, D. C.;* by Frederick J. V. Skiff, *director of the Field Columbian
Museum, Chicago,* and by the author.   Ethnological collections and
the best illustrative works on ethnological subjects scattered
throughout the country have been carefully searched for material.
Many of the text illustrations of this volume are reproductions
of originals found in the caves and rock shelters of France.

K. E. D.

October, 1906.

CONTENTS

THE LATER CAVE-MEN
THE AGE OF THE CHASE

FULL PAGE

"Pigeon boiled meat and gave it to the men, and they all sounded her praises." — *Page 166.*

THE LATER CAVE-MEN
THE AGE OF THE CHASE

I

The Reindeer Start for their Summer Home

Every winter the reindeer came to the wooded hills where the Cave-men lived. No matter how deep the snow, they always found food. Sometimes they stretched their slender necks and ate moss from the trees. Again they scraped up the snow with their forefeet and found dry grass.

The reindeer liked cold weather. They liked the north wind that brought the snow. As soon as the snow began to melt, they started toward the mountains. In the high valleys among the mountains, there was snow all the year round.

One morning the Cave-men awoke and found the south wind blowing. All the people were glad; for they knew it would drive the winter away.

The reindeer sniffed the warm wind and knew it was time to go. Each leader signaled to his herd. And soon the wooded hills were dotted with small herds moving toward the ford.

Straightshaft saw what the reindeer were doing and he signaled the news to the men. Then the Cave-men gathered around Scarface, who was to lead them in the hunt.

The children had listened to all that was said about the great herd. They could scarcely wait to see it. Fleetfoot pulled his grandmother's hand and started up the cliff. Chew-chew wanted to see the herds meet at the reindeer ford. All the women wanted to see the great herd before it went away. So they all climbed the cliff where they could get a good view.

When the children saw a herd near the river, they clapped their hands and shouted. Then Chew-chew pointed out many herds and they all danced for joy.

The scattered herds were coming slowly down the little valleys. Each followed a handsome leader headed toward the ford.

"Look!" said Chew-chew as the leader of a herd plunged into the river. The herd plunged too, for reindeer know it is best to follow their leader. The reindeer swam through the deep water and waded out to the opposite bank. Then the frightened creatures hurried on toward the well-known ford.

A reindeer.

"Why did the reindeer jump into the river?" asked Fleetfoot of Chew-chew. Before she could answer Eagle-eye pointed to a big cave-bear. The cave-bear was going into a thicket when Fleetfoot

"*The reindeer swam through the deep water and waded out to the opposite bank.*"

heard his mother say, "Cave-bears and hyenas hide in the thickets. They lie in wait for the herds."

Scarface seemed to be lying in wait on some rocks by an evergreen tree. He had stopped on his way to the reindeer pass to see what had frightened the herd.

While the men were going to the pass, the reindeer were gathering at the ford. Several herds of two or three hundred each were already there. Other herds were coming. The flat sandy banks on one side of the river were already covered with reindeer. Soon the ford was filled, and the reindeer began to press up the narrow river valley.

When at last all the herds from the wooded hills were gathered at the ford, the handsomest leader of all stepped forth to lead the way. After looking around to see if an enemy was near, he started up the well-trodden trail through the narrow river valley.

Slowly the great herd began to move. To those watching from the cliff, it looked like a moving forest. Those in advance were soon out of sight, and were going toward the pass.

Meanwhile the men had reached the pass where the bravest ones hid at the farther end. There they waited to spear the reindeer, while others hid behind rocks near the entrance to drive the reindeer on.

While the women and children watched from the cliff a signal came from the men. It was a call for the women to come and carry the reindeer to the cave. The younger women went, but Chew-chew stayed and watched with the children.

At length the Cave-men returned. The men brought trophies and the women brought heavy loads of meat. They found Chew-chew and the children still watching from the cliff. There they all watched for a long, long time; for not until the sun was low down in the sky had the last of the reindeer left the ford.

THINGS TO DO

Model a large river valley with many little valleys in it. Show where the small herds were. Model the cliffs along the river and show the flat sandy banks on one side, and the narrow valley with steep sides on the other.

Find rocks and make the reindeer pass. Make the trail from the ford through the narrow valley to the pass.

Play the story this lesson tells.

Draw one of these pictures:—

The reindeer stretched their slender necks and ate moss from the trees.

The reindeer sniffed the warm wind and knew it was time to go.

Fleetfoot pulled his grandmother's hand and started up the cliff.

The cave-bears and hyenas hide in the thickets.

Hunting at the reindeer pass.

Show how Eagle-eye loaded a reindeer upon her back. Model Eagle-eye in clay so as to show how she carried the reindeer.

II

THINGS TO THINK ABOUT

If you have read the story of "The Early Cave-men," tell how the cave that was flooded was made.

Can you think of any other way in which a cave might be made?

If you have ever seen a shallow hole in a cliff, see if you can find out how it was made. If such a hole was made in a very soft rock what would happen to it?   What would happen to a hole made in a hard rock?

See if you can find a piece of limestone.   What do we use limestone for?

If we wanted a house of limestone, what would we do to get it? When the Cave-men wanted a limestone house, what did they do?

Chew-chew

Chew-chew was the oldest woman in the cave at the Fork of the River.   She was not as strong as she once had been; but she was still able to lead the women in their work.   Her sons' wives carried the heaviest burdens, but Chew-chew still carried heavy loads.

Chew-chew was the wisest woman in the cave. When the other women did not know what to do, they always asked Chew-chew   The bravest men were always glad to get Chew-chew's advice.   The children thought nobody could tell such stories as Chew-chew told.

Chew-chew and all of her children belonged to the Horse clan.   All the children in those days took the clan name of their mother.   Chew-chew's sons had captured wives from the Reindeer clan.   And so the children in Chew-chew's cave belonged to the Reindeer clan.   It thus happened that in every cave there were people of different clans.   But since Chew-chew was the oldest woman in the cave, we shall call the people at the Fork of the River by the name of the Horse clan.

Chew-chew often told the children about her first home.   She told them about the cave near the River of Snow, which was much like the cave which sheltered

Chew-chew telling stories to Fleetfoot.

them.   She told them about the wide shelving rocks which were like the ones above their cave.   And she told how frightened her people were the day a rock fell near the mouth of their cave.

No one knew at the time what made the rock fall No one knew there was no need of being afraid.   Some one said that the god of the cliff was angry and that he had pushed the rock down   Everybody believed the story.   So nobody dared go near the cave.

But the Cave-men needed a shelter.   So they offered gifts to the god of the cliffs.   When they thought he was satisfied, they all went back to the cave   And after a while they used the big rock as a table for their work.

Chew-chew wanted the children to grow to be brave and wise.   So she told them stories of the bravest and wisest people of her clan.   She told them stories about their grandfathers who were the heroes of the olden times.   And Fleetfoot never grew tired of hearing about the wonderful things which his grandfathers did.

And so Chew-chew taught the children all she thought they ought to know.   And they looked into her eyes and listened to all that she said.

THINGS TO DO

If there are cliffs or shelving rocks near by, go and see them. Find places where you think caves may form.   Find out why it is that the rocks shelve.   Why does a shelving rock sometimes break and fall to the ground?

Model the cliffs which you find. Model a cave which is formed in a cliff.

Tell a story which you think Chew-chew might have told to the children.

Play one of these plays:—
  Chew-chew telling stories to the children.
  What the people did when the rock fell near the mouth of the cave.
Draw a picture of something which you have played.

III

THINGS TO THINK ABOUT

Why did Chew-chew tell the children stories about their forefathers?
Why do we like to hear such stories?

Do you think that the later Cave-men will hunt in just the same way that the early Cave-men did?

What change took place in the animals while the Cave-men were learning to be good hunters? What change did the Cave-men have to make in their hunting on account of this?

Of all the animals you know, which are the fastest runners? Can you think how they became fast runners?

Fleetfoot's Lessons

When the men were at home, Fleetfoot liked to stay with them. He liked to watch them make spears; he liked to watch them run races; he liked to listen to the stories they told about the wild animals.

When the men went out to hunt, Fleetfoot wanted to go with them. But he was a little boy, and had to stay at home. Sometimes he went with his mother when she went to dig roots; sometimes he went with her to gather twigs for baskets. But the safest place for little children was not far from the fire. So Fleetfoot stayed at home nearly all the time.

While the children played near the cave, Chew-chew broke fagots with a stone ax. When she was ready to sit down, they all gathered around her.

They knew that that was one of the times when Chew-chew told them stories.

This time Chew-chew began with a story of the early Cave-men. She told of animals that stood their ground and fought instead of running away. She told about the strong spears and axes made to conquer the wild beasts. She told of brave and daring deeds of the heroes of olden times.

None of the animals feared man before he had fire. And for a long time afterward none of them feared him without a torch. But the early Cave-men made strong weapons after they had fire. They struck hard blows with their stone axes, which the animals learned to fear.

A stone ax.

Grass-eating animals feared beasts of prey long before the Tree-dwellers lived. Wild horses learned to run fast by trying to escape from packs of wolves. They learned to keep sentinels to watch while the herd fed. All the grass-eating animals learned to do this. The sentinels signaled at a sign of danger, and then the herd ran; and so their enemies learned to hunt by following the chase.

When Chew-chew was tired of telling stories, she marked out a path for a race. Then she showed the children how to get a fair start, by standing abreast and holding a stick.

The children learned to keep in step until they reached the real starting place. Then they dropped the stick and ran. And they all clapped their hands and cheered the one who won the race.

"Then Scarface threw, and all the horses took fright."

After the children had raced a long time, they came back to Chew-chew for another story. And this time she told them stories about the men of their own clan. They often chased the animals from early morn until noon. At first they got very tired when they went on a long chase. But the more they practiced running, the better they hunted in the real chase.

When the story was ended, the children climbed the cliff. Chew-chew went with them and they all looked at the wild horses going up the trail.

The horses had been to the river to drink and now they were going away. They were following their leader up the trail which led to the grassy plains.

Chew-chew knew where the men were lying in wait and she pointed out the spot. The children looked just in time to see Straightshaft throw his spear. Then Scarface threw, and all the horses took fright.

Up hill and down, through bushes and briars, the horses galloped away. The Cave-men followed the wounded ones, hurling their spears as they ran.

The chase was long and weary, and some of the wounded horses escaped. But the men returned with many trophies and the women brought heavy loads of meat.

The trophies the Cave-men prized the most were the heads of the wild horses. They kept these trophies near the cave, and they thought that they were charms. The Cave-men thought that the horses' heads would bring more horses to the hunting grounds.

THINGS TO DO

Tell a story about the age of combat.   Tell a story about the age of the chase.   Draw a picture to illustrate each story.

Show on your sand map where the men were lying in wait for the horses.   Model the trail which the horses followed.

What chasing game do you know how to play?   Can you think how some of these games first started?

Why do people not try to run as fast in a long race as in a short one?

Model in clay something which you might name "The Age of Combat."

IV

THINGS TO THINK ABOUT

How do you feel after you have had a long, hard chase?

What does your mother tell you to do when you come in dripping with sweat?

How do you think the Cave-men learned to take care of themselves?

When they were lame and stiff, do you think they would know what made them so?   Think of as many things as you can that they might do to make themselves feel better.

After the Chase

When the long, hard chase was over, the Cave-men were tired and dripping with sweat.   All but Scarface threw themselves upon the cold ground to rest.

It was Scarface who blew the whistle which called the women to the spot.   It was he who guarded the carcasses until the women came.   And while the women skinned the horses he sat on a log to rest.

It was sunset when they reached the cave.   All joined in a feast upon horse flesh, then they slept until break of day. It was then that the men groaned with pain. Their muscles ached, and they were so lame that they could scarcely move. Scarface alone of all the men was not suffering with pain.

Perhaps you can tell what made the men lame. None of the Cave-men knew. Everybody thought that an angry god was trying to punish them.

And so the men tried to drive the god away by raising fearful shouts. Then they asked Chew-chew's advice, and Chew-chew took her basket and started up the dry ravine. There she found bitter roots which she gathered and carried home.

No one knew at that time how to steep roots, for people had not learned how to boil. So Chew-chew chopped the roots with a stone chopper and laid them upon hot stones. And while the men breathed the bitter fumes, Chew-chew threatened the angry god and commanded him to go away.

In a few days the men were well and it was almost time to go hunting again. Straightshaft feared the angry god. He talked with the men and they wondered why it was that Scarface escaped. They looked at his deep scar which a tiger's claw had made. And then they looked at the trophies of Scarface which he wore about his neck.

Every Cave-man admired the deep scar of the bravest man in the clan. Every man wished that he, too, could show such a scar as that. And the men began to wonder if the scar was a kind of a charm.

The more the men talked about the scar, the more

"*Chew-chew took her basket and started up the dry ravine.*"

they wanted scars. They talked with Chew-chew about it, and at last decided to let her make scars.

So Chew-chew muttered prayers to the gods, and asked them not to hurt the Cave-men. Then she took a flint point and scratched the men's arms until she made big scars.

Years afterward, when people made scars, they stained them with all sorts of things. Sometimes they stained the scars with juices of plants, and sometimes they colored them with paints.

The Cave-men thought they could protect themselves by scars, and by all sorts of charms. So they kept on making scars, and they hunted for all sorts of charms.

But no matter how many charms they wore, they often were lame and stiff. Some one must have noticed that they were more apt to be lame after sitting on the cold ground while they were warm. For after a while the custom grew of never sitting on the bare ground while they were warm.

THINGS TO DO

Draw or paint a pattern which you think the Cave-men might have tattooed upon their arms. Where do we put the pictures which we make?

Find and name as many roots and herbs as you can that are used as medicines.

What animals have you seen eating herbs?

What mistakes did the Cave-men make when they tried to cure themselves?

"*She took a flint point and scratched the men's arms until she made big scars.*"

V

THINGS TO THINK ABOUT

What way can you use a spear besides thrusting it with one or both hands?

What changes do you think the Cave-men made in their spearheads when they began to throw spears? What changes do you think they made in the shafts?

How do you think the Cave-men made straight shafts for their spears? What do we do with wood when we wish to bend it?

Why the Cave-men made Changes in their Weapons

While the Cave-men were resting from the hunt, they did a great many things. They practiced running; they hunted for stuff to make new weapons; they worked upon their weapons and trophies; they learned new hunting dances. No matter what they did, they always asked their gods to help.

All the later Cave-men learned to make light spears and javelins. The clumsy spear which served Strongarm so well was not what Scarface needed. But in the days of the early Cave-men the heavy spear was a good weapon. Strongarm cared as much for his spear as you do for your dog. It was like a friend in time of need. Few animals could withstand Strongarm's blow when he grasped his spear in one or both hands and lunged

A laurel leaf. *Laurel leaf-shaped spear point.*

A stone knife

forward with all his might.   His spear was a powerful weapon.   But Strongarm lived in the age of combat when people fought animals at close range.

The later Cave-men did not make light spears and javelins all at once.   They began by throwing heavy spears.   Chew-chew could tell of many a hunter who lost his life throwing a spear.   Sometimes it was because the spear was too heavy to throw with enough force.   Sometimes it was because the shaft was crooked and the spear did not go to the right spot.

When the Cave-men practiced throwing, they did not stand still and throw.   They took aim and threw as they ran.   That was the kind of practice they needed for the real chase.

The mark, too, was a moving mark.   It was made of a bundle of branches, or an old skin stuffed with leaves.   While one man dragged it by a long cord, the others ran after it, throwing their spears.

A Cave-man could wound an animal with a spear, but he could not give a deadly blow.   There was always danger of the wounded animal turning upon the hunter.   A skilled hunter with a good spear ran little risk in throwing it.   But not all the Cave-men had enough skill.   Not all of the Cave-men made good enough weapons to be thrown with a sure aim.

And so the Cave-men learned new ways of making and using spears.   Perhaps they did not want to do it.   But they had to do it or die.   So you see why the men and boys spent most of their time in learning to follow

the chase.   Even the women and girls learned to hunt
and to make all sorts of weapons.

Long before Scarface lived the Cave-men began to
make lighter spears.   The straighter they made the
shaft, the easier it was to hit the mark.   And so the
Cave-men began to vie with one another in making
the straightest and smoothest shafts.

When they cut the sticks for the shafts the Cave-
men made gifts to the wood-gods, and asked for
the straightest and toughest branches that grew
on the trees.   Then they cut the branches carefully and carried them home to the cave.   There
they peeled them from butt to tip and smoothed
them with stone scrapers.   Sometimes they rubbed
them with fat and laid them away to dry.   It was
hard work to make a crooked stick straight.
But the Cave-men tried many ways and at last
they learned to make as beautiful shafts as ever
have been made.

*A
stone scraper.*

When the Cave-men pulled the shaft back
and forth on the sandstone, they made deep grooves
in it.   We have found pieces of grooved sandstone
that the later Cave-men used.   Sometimes they
would clamp a crooked stick between a grooved piece
of sandstone and a flat bone.   Then they would
pull and twist, and pull and twist, and pull and
twist that stick back and forth until the crooked place
was made straight.

When Scarface was very old he made a shaft-
straightener of a piece of reindeer horn.   He carved

the head of the reindeer upon it, and made a hole
for the shaft.   Then he thrust the
crooked stick through the hole and
turned the shaft-straightener round and
round as we turn a wrench, until he
straightened the shaft.

*A
shaft-
straightener.*

THINGS TO DO

*See if you can find a good branch for a shaft.   If you have a right
to cut the branch, see if you can make it into a shaft.*

*Find a stone which you can use for a scraper.   What else can you use
as a scraper?*

*If you do not care to make a shaft, make something else out of the
stick which you straighten.*

Name the things which you have at home or at school made of wood.

Make a collection of the different kinds of wood which you know.

*Which of these are soft wood?   What do we use soft wood for?
Which are hard?   What do we use hard wood for?*

VI.

THINGS TO THINK ABOUT

Can you think why the Cave-men used stone for their spear points
and knives before they used bone or horn?

What tools did the Cave-men need in making flint spear points?

Why did the Cave-men have to learn to strike gentle blows in
making their weapons?   Can you think of any way of removing little
pieces of flint besides striking them off?

How the Cave-men made Delicate Spear Points

Perhaps you have seen very beautiful Indian arrows. Perhaps you have wished you could make such arrows yourself. The later Cave-men first made such weapons and no people since have ever been able to make more beautiful ones.

The early Cave-men did not need such beautiful spear points. Rough points of flint and heavy stone axes were the weapons they needed most. It was not until the Age of the Chase that people shaped stone into beautiful forms.

Scarface always used flakes of flint for the points of spears and javelins. But in earlier times, people did not know how to strike off flakes of flint. They put the flint on a hard rock and struck it with a heavy blow. They smashed the flint, for the hard rock did not yield. They had not learned to let the flint break in its own way.

When the Cave-men held the flint in the hand, the hand yielded to the light blow. The flint broke in its own way. But the sharp edges cut the men's hands. So they covered the palms of their hands with rawhide and kept from getting hurt. When they worked in this way, they had no trouble in striking off flakes for spear points and knives.

When the men worked on their flint points, Fleetfoot liked to play near the workshop. He

A delicate spearhead

liked to watch Straightshaft strike off flakes with a hammer-stone and punch. He liked to listen to the song that Scarface and Straightshaft sang.

Scarface and Straightshaft always sang when they worked with the hammer-stone and punch. While Scarface placed the punch he sang in low tones. And when he was ready for Straightshaft to strike, he sang so as to let him know. Then Straightshaft took up the song and marked the time for each blow.

The men always sang when they worked together. If one man stopped when it was his turn to sing, the other did not know what to do. Besides marking the time, the song helped the men to measure the force of each blow. It helped them to strike off tiny flakes so as not to break the point. So, at length, the Cave-men began to think that the song they sang was a charm.

"When the Cave-men held the flint in the hand, the hand yielded to the light blow."

"While Scarface placed the punch he sang in low tones."

While the men struck off large flint flakes, Fleetfoot played not far away. He played while they hafted long narrow flakes for knives, but when they began to chip spearheads, he came and watched them at their work. He listened to the song of Scarface and Straightshaft, while they shaped a fine spearhead.

At length the spearhead was ready for the finishing touches. So Straightshaft dropped his hammerstone and picked up a queer little tool. He called it a flaker, and he used it to press off tiny flakes from the beautiful point.

When Straightshaft had finished, he dropped the flaker and Fleetfoot picked it up. And he asked Straightshaft if he might use it to press off little flakes.

Straightshaft let him try, but Fleetfoot was not strong enough to press off hard flint flakes. So he listened to the story that Scarface told of the young man who first made a flaker.

Holding up a little bone flaker, Scarface turned to the men and said: "When I was a boy, no one pressed off flakes of flint. No one had a flaker. We hammered off flint flakes.

"One summer when there were plenty of salmon, the neighboring clans had a great feast. Nimble-finger came. I saw him. I heard him speak. The third day of the feast I saw him flake flint."

Straightshaft using a flaker.

As Scarface went on he told how Nimble-finger
invented the flaker. He did it one day when he
was making a bone handle for a knife. When
he was scraping a bone with a flint scraper he
happened to press off a flint flake.

Nimble-finger did not know how it happened.
He tried again and again. At last he pressed off
another flake; and this time he knew that he did
it by pressing the point of the bone against one
edge of the flint.

Nimble-finger never finished that bone-handled
hunting knife. But he showed the people how
to make a flaker. He became an inventor; for
he gave the world a tool it had never had before.

When the people returned from the feast many
forgot about the flaker. Others longed for delicate
spear points like those Nimble-finger made. So,
at length, they tried to make flakers of their own.
Some tried to make them of wood; but the wood
was too soft to break the stone. Others tried to
make them of ivory; but ivory was too hard to get
a hold. At length all the Cave-men made flakers
of antler and bone, for they were hard enough to break
the stone and soft enough to get a hold.

A flaker.

When Scarface finished, Fleetfoot began to talk
about Nimble-finger. He asked Scarface, "Where
does Nimble-finger live? Does he always come to the
great feasts?"

To the child's questions Scarface replied, "While
Nimble-finger was still a young man he went far away.

For many years he lived far north in a cave beside the River of Stones. But years have come and gone since then. If he still lives, he is an old man; but of that I know not."

THINGS TO DO

If you can find a piece of flint strike off a flake with a hammer-stone.   Strike off a flake with an angular stone.   Strike off a flake by using a hammer and punch.

Sort out the flakes that are good for knives.   Put handles on them. Sort out the flakes that are good for making into spearheads.   See if you can strike off tiny flakes until the large flake looks like a spearhead.

Find something which you can use as a flaker.   When you have made one, see if you can use it.

Make a collection of stones which you can chip or flake.   Tell all you know about each of those stones.

Think of Scarface as he was telling the story.   Draw the picture.

VII

THINGS TO THINK ABOUT

What do our horses and cattle eat?   Where do we get their food? What do wild cattle and horses eat?   See if you can find out whether wild cattle or horses have ever lived in a place where the ground is covered with snow part of the year.

Did you ever see cattle pawing the ground?   Did you ever see horses pawing the ground?   Did you ever see them paw the snow?

See if you can find out something about the great herds of bison that used to live in this country.   What has become of them?

Can you think why bison live in herds?   What officers does a herd of bison have?   Can you think how the officers of a herd of bison are chosen?

The Return of the Bison

Ever since the reindeer went away the Cave-men had been looking for the return of the bison. Each summer the herds came up the valley to feed on green grass and tender shoots. Each winter they went to the forests of the lowlands where they found shelter from the cold.

The snow was now gone from the wooded hills and the days were warm again. The dingy brown coats of the hillsides were changing to the palest green. The buds were beginning to swell. Everything seemed to say that summer was coming.

Each day the Cave-men watched for signs of the coming of the great herd. Each night they danced the bison dance and tried to make the bison come.

One morning Straightshaft climbed the cliff and looked far up and down the valley. Looking north he could see the River of Stones with high cliffs on one or both banks. He could see dense forests of evergreen that grew on the low banks. He could see hills and valleys beyond the cliffs where many wild animals lived.

Looking south, near at hand, was the Fork of the River where Little River joined the River of Stones. Here the cliffs were not very high; farther down, they became lower, and at last there were no cliffs. The edge of the lowland forest where the bison wintered could be seen far away. Grassy lowlands near the forests stretched farther than the eye could see. It was here that the bison and cattle found the best winter

" Straightshaft saw the herd at sunrise and made a sign to the men."

pastures. It was in the lowland forests that they found shelter from the cold.

Straightshaft looked toward the lowlands, hoping to see a bison. Mammoths were feeding not far away, and beyond were woolly rhinoceroses. But there was not one bison.

As Straightshaft watched the second day, chamois and ibexes played on the hills. Herds of horses came from the grassy uplands and returned after drinking at the ford. But no sign of a bison yet appeared.

The third day Straightshaft saw a black spot in the distance. It was far down on the river trail. As he watched, it became larger and larger. And then Straightshaft knew that it was a bison coming in advance of the great herd.

An ibex.

The morning of the fourth day the great herd came. A powerful bison led the way. Strong sentinels guarded either side. The herd followed blindly, galloping eight or ten abreast.

Straightshaft saw the herd at sunrise and made a sign to the men. Those who saw it passed it along, and soon all the people had seen the sign. Then everybody climbed up a hill or a high cliff and watched the coming of the bison.

Nearer and nearer the great herd came, like a sea of tossing manes and horns. The earth trembled beneath their tread and the air was filled with their bellowing.

When the bison reached the ford, the foremost creatures stopped to drink. But the solid mass, pressing on from the rear, crowded them up the river. Soon the ford was packed with struggling beasts. Some tried to escape by swimming up the river. Others swam down the stream. And still the solid mass from the rear kept crowding on and on.

At length the herd divided. One part followed the river trail, while the other went up the narrow valley. Whenever a herd reached a branching valley, a big bison led off a small herd. This happened many a time. And at the close of the day there was not a little valley in the surrounding country that did not have a herd of two or three hundred bison.

THINGS TO DO

Play you are a herd of bison, and show how the herd marched. Show how it divided. Show how you think it would come together again.

Show in your sand-box where Straightshaft stood while he watched. Show the trails the bison followed.

Think of the herd as it galloped up the river trail. Draw the picture. Make such a sign as you think Straightshaft made.

Plan a bison dance.

VIII

THINGS TO THINK ABOUT

If you were to hunt bison, what would you want to know about them?

In what ways can bison notice signs of danger? In what ways can they help one another?

Watch animals, and see if they give signs to one another.

What weapons do you think the Cave-men would take when they went to hunt the bison? How could the Cave-men help one another in hunting? How might one man hinder the others?

"*At the close of the day there was not a little valley in the surrounding country that did not have a herd of two or three hundred bison.*"

The First Bison Hunt of the Season

And now the great herd of bison had come, and the
Cave-men were eager to hunt them. While they were
getting ready to start they kept up this merry song :—

> *The bison have come;*
> *The bison have come;*
> *Now for the chase!*
> *Now for the chase!*
> *Bring axes and spears;*
> *Bring axes and spears;*
> *Now for the chase!*
> *Now for the chase!*

When Scarface climbed the cliff he saw three herds
of bison. The first was feeding in an open space; the
second was on a hillside, and the third was in a narrow
valley close by a deep and hidden ravine. This was a
place where the Cave-men liked to hunt. So they
agreed to follow Scarface through the hidden ravine.

Scarface led the way, and all the men followed. Not
a leaf rustled beneath their tread. Not a twig broke as
they crept up the side of the deep ravine and looked
out at the herd.

Everybody wanted to get the yearlings or young
cows, for their flesh was tender and sweet. But the
cows and young bison were in the center of the herd.
They were guarded by the sentinels, whose flesh was
hard and tough.

And so the Cave-men wondered how to get a young
bison. They wondered if the vigilant leader was more

"With a quick snort he turned and charged."

than a match for them.   They watched his signals, and saw fresh sentinels take the places of the hungry ones.   They noticed how quickly the bison obeyed every signal the leader gave.

At last the Cave-men decided to attack the leader first.   They waited till he was not more than a stone's throw away.   Then Scarface gave the signal and the men made a bold attack.

Straightshaft hurled his spear with all his might, then turned to give place to the others.   The leader was taken by surprise.   The men had crept up so quietly that not till the spear whizzed through the air did he suspect danger.

With a quick snort he turned and charged.   Straight-shaft ran, but the others met the charge.   They hurled their spears and dealt heavy blows with their stone axes.

Before the leader could give the alarm he lay stretched out on the ground.   The sentinels looked for a signal.   Meanwhile the cows and yearlings tried to make their escape.

Then each of several sentinels tried to lead.   But the frightened herd did not know which one to follow. Some of the bison rushed one way and some rushed another.   Then there was a general stampede.   They gored one another with their sharp horns.   They trampled one another under their feet.   They were too frightened to know what they were doing.

It was then that the Cave-men singled out the young bison.   When they had secured them for their prize, they started toward the cave, singing—

To-day we went hunting.
We crept up the ravine;
We surprised the leader of the bison.
He made a charge upon us —
We have his horns for a headdress.
We killed many a young bison;
We have plenty of tender meat.

Perhaps one of the sentinels became leader of the herd that very day. Perhaps several battles were fought to see which sentinel was the strongest. For bison never follow a leader that is not stronger and wiser than themselves.

THINGS TO DO

Show in your sand-box where each of the three herds was feeding.
Make a plan for hunting the herd that was feeding in an open space.
Draw one of these pictures:—
The Cave-men creeping up the banks of the steep ravine.
The charge of the leader.
The stampede.
Deciding which bison shall be leader of the herd.
Make a song to sing in getting ready to hunt the way you have planned. Make a song to sing on your return.
Model a large, strong bison.

IX

THINGS TO THINK ABOUT

Watch water when it is boiling, and see if you can tell what happens.
Why would it be harder for people to learn to boil than to roast?
What kind of dishes did the Cave-men have?   What would happen to them if they were put over the fire?

What does your mother do, when she wants to find out whether the flatiron is hot enough to iron?

When the Cave-men first learned to boil water, do you think they would think of boiling food? What might make them think of boiling food?

What Happened when the Children Played with Hot Stones

Again the Cave-men went out to hunt. Again the women went out to gather roots and berries. Only Chew-chew and the children were left near the cave.

Chew-chew was curing the skins which the women had brought home. Some of them were stretched out on the ground. Others were stretched on frames. Many of these were ready to be rolled up and put away.

While the skins were drying, Chew-chew had time for other work. She wanted to finish her basket, and so the splints must be put to soak.

At a sign from Chew-chew, Fleetfoot went to the river for a bag of water. While he was gone, Chew chew began to make a place to put it. She dug a shal-low hole in the ground and lined it with a skin.

When Fleetfoot came back they patted down the skin. Then they poured the water into the skin-lined hole, and put the splints to soak.

While Chew-chew worked at her basket, Fleetfoot played near at hand. Often he came to his grand-mother's side and talked about many things.

At length Chew-chew, holding up a skin, turned to

Fleetfoot and said, "Do you know what animal wore this skin?"

"One of the reindeer we saw at the ford," quickly responded Fleetfoot.

"Where have all the reindeer gone?" was Chew-chew's next question.

"To the cave of the Big Bear of the mountains," came the prompt answer.

While Chew-chew and Fleetfoot talked the children played near the cave. Pigeon was playing with stones which she had gathered and tossed into the fire. In trying to get them out again she burned her fingers, and began to cry.

When Chew-chew saw what had happened, she told Fleetfoot to play with Pigeon. And Fleetfoot played with Pigeon, and he showed her how to lift hot stones without getting burned.

A bear's tooth awl.

The children played and carried hot stones with tongs made of sticks. They ran back and forth between rows of skins until Pigeon dropped a hot stone into the hole.

No sooner had Pigeon dropped the stone than she screamed, "A snake! a snake!" And she ran to her grandmother and sobbed, while she hid her face in her chubby arm.

Chew-chew thought that a snake was crawling about. Fleetfoot helped her look under all the skins. They looked for some time, but they found no trace of a snake.

Then Chew-chew asked Pigeon to tell her all about it. And Pigeon said, "A big snake hissed and made me drop the stone."

Just then Fleetfoot dropped a hot stone and something went "s-s-s-s-s-s."

Pigeon screamed again, but a hearty laugh from Chew-chew showed there was nothing to fear. Chew-chew knew that the hissing sound was not the hiss of a snake. It was the sizzling of the water when it touched the hot stone.

And so Chew-chew tried to teach the children how to know the hissing sound. She picked up hot stones and dropped them into the water. Each time a stone was dropped, the hissing sound was heard; and the children learned to know the sound, and they were no longer afraid.

As Chew-chew kept on dropping the hot stones, she did not notice all that happened. She thought only of teaching the children, so that they would not be afraid. But at last such a strange thing happened, that even Chew-chew was afraid.

The water no longer was still. It kept moving like the angry water in the rapids of the river. A thin mist began to rise, and a strange voice came from the water, saying:—

"Bubble, bubble, bubble;
Bubble, bubble, bubble."

At the sound Chew-chew was filled with fear. She was afraid the gods were angry. She looked about for an offering, and found a piece of bison meat. She

"Chew-chew tried to teach the children how to know the hissing sound."

dropped the meat into the water, hoping to appease the angry god.

The bubbling ceased, but Chew-chew was still afraid. So she called the children together, and took them into the cave.

When the men and women came home that night, Chew-chew told them what had happened. They went to the spot and saw the meat, which they thought the god had left. Then they listened in silence as Chew-chew told them the story again and again.

THINGS TO DO

Choose some one for each of the parts and dramatize the story.
Draw pictures which will show what happened.
See if you can boil water by dropping hot stones into it.
Show in your sand-box how the skins were stretched out, and how the skin-lined hole was made.

X

THINGS TO THINK ABOUT

What do you think Chew-chew might learn by dropping the meat into the hot water?

What kind of boiling-pots did people first use?

Why didn't they hang their boiling-pots over the fire?

Why the Children Began to Eat Boiled Meat

The more Chew-chew thought about the bubbling sound, the more she wanted to hear it again She wondered what the god wanted to say, and if he was asking for food. She wondered if she could make friends with him by giving him something to eat.

Chew-chew talked with Eagle-eye and at length they tried to make friends with the god. They prepared a place for the water by making a skin-lined hole. Eagle-eye poured the water into the hole, while Chew-chew dropped in a piece of meat. Then they looked and listened for a sign, but no sign was made. They tried it again and again, but still there was no sign.

At length Chew-chew thought of the hot stones she had dropped when she heard the voice. So she and Eagle-eye heated stones and dropped them into the water. As they did it they muttered prayers to the gods and asked them to protect the Cave-men.

Before the women had dropped many stones, the children crowded around. Nobody was frightened this time when the hissing sound was heard. But their eyes opened wide when the water began to bubble.

Chew-chew dropped the meat into the water as an offering to the god. Everybody watched as she dropped the meat. Everybody breathed more freely when the bubbling ceased. And Chew-chew said, "The god is pleased with the offering of meat."

Many times after that Chew-chew dropped hot stones into the water, and offered meat to the god. But when she did it she never thought that she was cooking meat. She thought she was helping the Cave-men by winning the favor of the god.

Sometimes when the children were hungry, Chew-chew let them tear off strips of partly boiled meat. Sometimes she let them drink the broth from bone dippers and horns.

The children liked to eat the boiled meat and to drink the rich broth. But they always thought the meat and broth were what the god had left.

THINGS TO DO

Make tongs out of sticks and see if you can lift small objects with them.

Watch water when it boils, and tell where the steam comes from. Where does it go? Hold a cold plate over the steam and see what happens. Where do the drops of water on the plate come from?

When water stands in the open air, what becomes of part of it?

Why do we hang clothes out on the clothes-line to dry?

What becomes of the water that was in the clothes?

Tell what you think happens just as clouds form. See if you can do something that will show what happens at the time.

What happens to the clouds just as it begins to rain?

XI

THINGS TO THINK ABOUT

Why would the grass-eating animals go from place to place during the summer? What do you think the Cave-men would do when the herds went away?

At what season of the year are nuts fit to gather? Is there any place near by where you have a right to go nutting?

What animals eat nuts? What animals store nuts? Do you think the Cave-men would gather many nuts?

The Nutting Season

Summer passed as summers had passed before. When the bison went to the higher lands, the Cave-men followed them. When they started toward their winter pastures, the Cave-men came home.

"All the women and children went nutting."

It was the nutting season when they returned. All the beech, walnut, and butternut trees were heavily laden that year. The ground underneath their branches was nearly covered with nuts. Slender hazel bushes bent under their heavy loads.

Wild hogs and bears had begun to harvest the nuts before the Cave-men returned. Each day they went to the trees and ate the nuts that had fallen. When Eagle-eye saw what they were doing, she said, "Bring your bags and baskets and come. If we do not look out the hogs will get the best of the nuts this year."

Then all the women and children went nutting. They gathered the nuts that lay upon the ground and put them in their baskets. Some climbed trees and shook the branches until they got a shower of nuts; others took their digging sticks and beat the heavily laden branches.

The children had a feast that day. They sat down under the trees and cracked all the nuts they could eat. They gathered handfuls and helped their mothers fill baskets and skin bags. They climbed the trees and they laughed and played all day long.

When the women first came to the trees, they heard the wild hogs in the distance. Once a big hog came up and tried to eat the nuts out of a basket. But Eagle-eye chased him with a big stick and drove him away from the spot.

When Eagle-eye was coming back from the chase, she saw other trees heavily laden. She called to the women, and they came to the spot and forgot all about the nuts they had gathered.

The wild hogs were having a feast.

It was Chew-chew who first thought of the pile of nuts they had left on the ground. It was she who ran to the trees and found the wild hogs having a feast.

Chew-chew struck one of the hogs with her digging stick. He was munching the nuts she had gathered. He turned away and she struck another; then the first hog came back.

Chew-chew soon found that unless she had help the hogs would eat all the nuts, for as fast as she drove one hog away another one came back. Chew-chew screamed for help and the women came with their digging-sticks.

The women drove the hogs away, but they returned again and again. And so the women learned to keep a close watch while they were gathering nuts. But in spite of all their trouble, they had a good time that day.

It was not until they were starting home that they found that a serious thing had happened. They did not know all about it then, and some of them never knew.

' It was all about Fleetfoot. When Eagle-eye looked for him, he was nowhere to be seen. At first she thought he was with Chew-chew, but Chew-chew had not seen him since morn.

Fleetfoot had played near his mother nearly all day. He had cracked nuts; he had climbed trees; he had mimicked the squirrels; he had scattered burrs in the rabbits' paths, and he had done all sorts of things.

But now Fleetfoot was lost, and everybody began to hunt for him. Eagle-eye found the stones he had left

only a short time before. She found his tracks and followed them until they crossed the boundary of the hunting ground. There she lost all trace of him. She called,
but the "caw-caw" of a crow was the only answer.

The men heard her call, and came to join in the
search. But in spite of all they could do, they did not
find the child.

And so the Cave-men thought they would never see
Fleetfoot again. They thought he had lost his way in
the forest and had been killed by a cave-bear. For a
few days they mourned for the child, then they spoke
no more of him.

THINGS TO DO

Tell a story of what happened one time when you went nutting.
Name all the nuts you can that grow on trees.   Name those that
grow on bushes.   Where do peanuts grow?
Dramatize this story.
Draw a picture of the part you like the best.

XII

THINGS TO THINK ABOUT

Why do people put up such signs as " Keep off," " Do not trespass"?
Why do people build fences around their land?

Do you think the Cave-men could hunt wherever they chose?
Why did each clan have its own hunting ground?   What kind of
boundaries did the hunting grounds have?   Why was it not safe to go
on the land of a stranger?

Why did mothers teach their children the boundary lines?

What do you think some mothers mean when they tell their children that the " Bogie-man" will get them?

Why Mothers Taught their Children the Boundary Lines

Each day brought so many hard things to do that most of the Cave-men forgot Fleetfoot. But his mother and grandmother did not forget him. They often thought of the boy they had lost.

Other mothers were afraid they might lose their children. So they tried to keep them from running away. Most of all, they tried to keep them from running across the boundary line.

When Pigeon tried to run away, Eagle-eye would say, "The cave-bear will get you." Mothers tried all sorts of ways to keep their children from danger.

Each clan had its own hunting ground. The people who lived together shared it, but no one else was allowed to hunt on the land. It was not even safe to cross the land of a stranger. Sometimes the Cave-men had to do it. Sometimes they had to call upon their neighbors for help. But since there were people who had lost their lives when trying to cross the land of strangers, the Cave-men learned to use signs to show what they wanted. They carved pictures upon sticks, which told what we might tell in a letter.

When a stranger carried a message-stick, it was safe for him to do his errand. People knew what he wanted and why he came, so they let him go on his way unharmed. But when a stranger had no message-stick, his life was not safe in a strange land.

" *Mothers taught their children what the boundaries were.*"

And so people learned to stay on their own lands, and mothers taught their children what the boundaries were. They taught the children to name them over and over again. They taught them to know how the boundaries looked.

For a long time Pigeon had to tell her mother each day the boundaries of the hunting grounds. She would stand on the cliff and point north to the narrow valley, then south to Little River. Then she pointed to a high ridge of hills toward the east and west to the River of Stones.

While Pigeon was so small that Eagle-eye had to take her by the hand, her mother took her to the boundaries. Eagle-eye had taught her so well that she knew them as soon as she saw them.

Perhaps you have heard the story told about mothers who taught their children the boundary lines. It is told that mothers used to be so anxious to have their children remember the boundaries that they whipped them at each one. Then the story is told that in later times instead of beating the children, people let them beat the boundaries. Some day you may be able to learn more about the strange customs of beating the boundary lines.

THINGS TO DO

Mark out in your sand-box the boundary lines of the hunting ground of the Horse clan. Show a good place for another hunting ground.

Ask some one to read you the story, " The Goblins will get you if you don't watch out." What do you think the story means?

Climb a hill, or look out of a high window, and see if you can find land which at one time was a good hunting ground.

See if you can make a message-stick.

XIII

THINGS TO THINK ABOUT

What do you think had happened to Fleetfoot?
If strangers found him, what do you think they would do with him?

What Happened to Fleetfoot

Perhaps you have been wondering what happened to Fleetfoot. Perhaps you would like to know how he happened to wander away from his clan.

It happened in this way. He cracked all the nuts he could eat; he climbed trees; he threw sticks and stones; he watched the wild hogs eating nuts; he listened to the whistle which Scarface blew to call the men to the hunt. He wished that he could blow the whistle and hunt with the men.

Then a rabbit hopped across his path and stopped and looked at him. How Fleetfoot longed to catch the rabbit and to hold him in his hands! He stood perfectly still; he could hear himself breathe; he tried to breathe more quietly, for he did not want to frighten the rabbit.

The rabbit started. How Fleetfoot wished he would go down the path where he had scattered burrs! But the rabbit took another path and Fleetfoot ran to catch him. He was almost sure he could lay his hands on the rabbit's stumpy white tail.

The rabbit was too quick for him, yet Fleetfoot did not give up He started on a hard chase and forgot about everything else. Up hill and down the rabbit

5

ran and Fleetfoot followed after.   Not until the rabbit was out of sight did Fleetfoot give up the chase.   Then he stopped and rested a while and tried to get his breath.

While Fleetfoot was resting he looked at the squirrels which were chattering in the trees.   He watched them hold nuts with their forepaws while they gnawed through the shells.   He listened to their chattering and then he wandered on.

Fleetfoot did not know that he had crossed the narrow valley.   He did not know that he had wandered into a strange land.   He thought nothing about where he was until some time had passed.   But after a while everything seemed still, and Fleetfoot began to feel lonesome.   And so he turned around to go back to the women and children.

Fleetfoot walked and walked, but he did not find them.   He called, but no answer came.   So he wandered on and on.

Soon Fleetfoot knew he was in a spot he had never seen before.   Everything seemed strange.   He looked this way and that; but he could not tell which way to go.   And so the lost child wandered farther and farther away from home.

He was choking down a sob when he caught sight of some women with packs upon their backs.   Fleetfoot thought he had found his people going home with their loads of nuts.   He ran and called to his mother.

A strange woman stopped and looked at the child. Then she gave a signal to her clan.

Fleetfoot was within reach of the strange woman

"A big man caught him, and put him upon his shoulder."

before he saw his mistake. He tried to run away. But he could not do it. A big man caught him and lifted him up and put him upon his shoulder. Strange men, women, and children crowded around and stared into his face.

Bighorn asked him where he lived; but Fleetfoot was too frightened to speak. He remembered the stories Chew-chew had told about strange clans. He wondered what the strangers would do. How he wished he were safe at home!

But poor Fleetfoot did not see his home again for many long years. He was in a strange land, and soon he was traveling with the strangers far away from his home.

A woman, whose name was Antler, took charge of Fleetfoot. She took him by the hand until he was too tired to walk. Then she carried him until they came to the place where they camped for the night.

THINGS TO DO

Choose some one for each of the parts and see if you can act out this story. Draw pictures to illustrate the story.

Name the wild animals you can find in your neighborhood. Notice what they eat. Do they help or harm the people near where they live? Model one of these animals in clay.

XIV

THINGS TO THINK ABOUT

What kind of a shelter do you think the people will have for the night?

Think of as many easy ways as you can of making a shelter out of trees.

How the Strangers Camped for the Night

The camping place was an old one.   It had been used many times.   The strange clan always used it on their way to and from the lowland plains.   It was under a big oak tree, and near a spring of fresh water.

When the strangers reached the camp, Greybeard took charge of Fleetfoot.   The women quickly unloaded their packs, and began to build a tent.

It did not take long to make the tent, for it was almost ready-made.   It was an old oak, which reached out long and low-spreading branches.   The branches had been bent to the ground many times, and now they nearly touched it.   So all that the women had to do was to fasten the ends firmly.   They did it by rolling a stone over the end of a branch, and sometimes they tied the end of a branch to a peg which they had driven in the ground.

All the Cave-men made such tents in the summer when they were away from the caves.   When the branches were not thick enough for a shelter, the women broke saplings and leaned them against the tree.

While Chipper worked at a spearhead, the other men were moving about.   Bighorn feared that Fleetfoot's clan might follow their tracks.

Long after Fleetfoot fell asleep, the strangers talked quietly.   They held their ears close to the ground and listened.   They went and looked at Fleetfoot, now fast asleep.   Then they all sat down by the fire.

"The tent was an old oak, which reached out long and low-spreading branches."

At length the men turned to Greybeard. And Grey-beard spoke to them and said, "When I was young my clan lived in a cave near Sweet Briar River. Every year, in the salmon season, the neighboring clans met at the rapids. The Horse clan came from the Fork of the River, where the Sweet Briar joins the River of Stones. They may live there still. This boy may belong to them."

"Do you think they will follow us?" asked Bighorn.

Greybeard looked up, but did not speak. He seemed to be trying to think. At length he turned to the men and said, "Sleep until the moon sets; I'll watch and wake you."

So the Cave-men went to the tent and slept while Greybeard kept watch. Not a sound escaped his ear that night. Not a leaf rustled that he did not hear. Not a twig broke, as wild animals passed, but that he found out what it meant.

As Greybeard watched in the moonlight he heard many a familiar sound. Now he heard the roar of a tiger, and again the "hoo-hoo" of an owl; now the howling of hyenas, and again an eagle's scream.

Among all these sounds Greybeard heard nothing that seemed to come from the lost child's clan. But when the moon was set he roused the people, and under cover of the darkness they hurried toward home.

They let Fleetfoot sleep, for fear he might answer if he were called. And so the child slept while he was hurried away through the darkness. At daybreak, when he awoke, he found himself in a new home.

THINGS TO DO

See if there is a tree in your neighborhood that could be made into such a tent as the Cave-men made.
Find a thick branch and make such a tent in your sand-box.
Draw one of these pictures:—
The council of the clan before going to sleep.
Greybeard watching in the moonlight.
Hurrying home under cover of the darkness.
Fleetfoot awakes and finds himself in his new home.
Act out part of this story and let some one guess what it is.
Write as many calls of the birds as you know.   Model one of the birds in clay.   If you know its nest, model that.

XV

THINGS TO THINK ABOUT

How do you think Fleetfoot felt the first few days he was with the strange clan?

What do you think he will learn of them?   What do you think he can teach them?

Fleetfoot is Adopted by the Bison Clan

For a few days Fleetfoot missed his mother and Chew-chew more than he could tell.   He missed little Pigeon, too.   He missed the people he had always seen. But he said very little about them.

It was Greybeard who told him that he was now living with the Bison clan.   Not all of the people belonged to that clan, but there were more of that clan than of any other.   And so they were known as the Bison clan.

At first Fleetfoot was afraid of the men and large boys. Most of all he was afraid of Bighorn, for it was Bighorn who captured him.

But before one moon had passed, he was adopted by the Bison clan. And soon after that, he began to feel at home. Greybeard told him stories, and gave him little spears. Antler was kind to him, and the children were always ready to play.

Fleetfoot liked to play with the children. He liked to play with Flaker best of all. Flaker was Antler's child, and he was about the size of Fleetfoot.

As the days became cold, the women worked upon skins. There was not a smooth spot near the cave which was not covered with a skin. Fleetfoot watched Antler as she cut little slits in the edges. He helped stretch the skins out on the ground and drive little pegs through the slits. He watched her stretch a skin on a frame and put it near the fire.

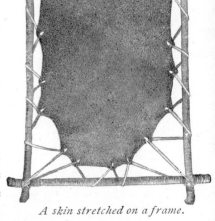

A skin stretched on a frame.

Antler scraped a skin until the fat was off, and the inner skin was removed. Then she roughened it by scraping it crosswise, so as to make it flexible.

A scraper.

When Fleetfoot saw Antler roll the skins in a loose roll, he asked if she was going to chew them. Antler smiled as she asked Fleetfoot how his mother softened skins.

Fleetfoot showed how his mother did it. And he told Antler about Chew-chew. He told her that Chew-chew got her name because she learned to chew the skins.

While Antler and Fleetfoot were talking, all the women and children gathered around. They wanted to see what they were doing, and to hear what Fleet-foot said.

Then Antler said to the women and children, "These skins are ready to soften. Come, join hands and show Fleetfoot how we soften hard skins."

What a noisy time they had for a little while! Each group wanted to finish first. Some of them stamped the skins, and kept time by singing. Others pounded the skins with their hands, and still others pounded with hammers of reindeer horn.

A hammer of reindeer horn.

They had such a merry time that Fleetfoot could not keep still. He was soon stamping and singing as well as any one.

When the skins were softened, Antler told Fleetfoot that once her people chewed the skins. But since they had found an easier way, they chewed only the edges they wished to sew.

And so Fleetfoot began to learn lessons of the Bison clan. But once he was the teacher. It was when he showed Flaker what happened the day Pigeon played with hot stones. Flaker told his mother, and Antler told Greybeard. And then Greybeard asked Fleetfoot to drop the hot stones in the water again.

All the Cave-men gathered around to see what Fleetfoot did. When the steam began to rise from the water, they stepped back. But when they saw that the child was not afraid, they came forward cautiously.

When the water began to bubble, they were all filled with fear. They looked upon Fleetfoot in silence. They called him a wonderful child.

THINGS TO DO

Tell a story about dressing skins. Draw pictures which will show all that is done in dressing the skin.

Dramatize the part of the story that tells what Fleetfoot taught the Bison clan. Draw a picture of it.

Make a song that people might sing in stamping upon the skins.

Make a song to sing while beating the skins.

XVI

THINGS TO THINK ABOUT

What kind of clothes do you wear in winter? What do you think the Cave-men wore? Can you think how they learned to fit skins to their bodies? What part of an animal's skin could they use for sleeves? What part could they use for leggings?

How do you think they learned to make mittens and gloves?

How many ways do you know of fastening garments? Which of these do we use? Which of these do you think the Cave-men used?

What did they use instead of a needle? What kind of thread did they have?

"*Greybeard asked Fleetfoot to drop the hot stones in the water again.*"

How the Cave-men Protected Themselves from the Cold

One morning Fleetfoot started out of the cave, but a cold wind drove him back. Snow had fallen during the night, and the air had grown very cold. It was not fit for a bare-backed boy to go out on such a day. So Fleetfoot stayed in the cave all day long.

All the Cave-men stayed in the cave nearly all the day. Once Chipper went out and found fresh tracks. He followed the tracks until he came within close range of a reindeer. But his bare arms shook with the cold, and he missed his aim.

The next day was bitterly cold. The river was frozen almost into silence. Only the ripples of the swiftest currents laughed aloud at the frost. The snow was deep on the hillsides. It was deeper in the valleys, and the narrow ravines were almost filled with snow.

The third day was still very cold and everybody was hungry and cross. The children were crying for food, and since Antler had nothing to give them, she was trying to get them to play.

At length the children began to take turns at playing they were cave-bears. Now it was Fleetfoot's turn to be the bear, and when Antler saw him she laughed.

The Cave-men looked up in surprise. Everybody was so hungry and cross it seemed strange to hear any one laugh. But Antler really was laughing.

Fleetfoot had found a cave-bear's skin on a ledge in

the cave. He had wrapped it around him so that he looked like a little cave-bear. The children kept calling him "little bear," and he was trying to act like one.

Soon all the people were laughing. They forgot, for the time, how hungry they were. And the next day they had meat, for it was warm enough to go hunting.

Many times after that the children played cave-bear. Many times the people laughed when they saw the children dressed in cave-bears' skins. Once when Antler looked at them, she got an idea about making clothes.

When Antler took a large skin and wrapped it around her, Fleetfoot thought that she was going to play bear." But Antler was not playing. She was thinking of the cold days when the children had no food. She was thinking that if she could make a warm dress, perhaps she could go out in the bitter cold.

Antler talked with Birdcatcher about it, and Birdcatcher helped her fit the skin. Birdcatcher fitted the skin of the head over Antler's head so as to make a warm hood. Then she run a cord through the slits along the edges and tied the ends under Antler's chin.

Antler fastened the skin down the front with buckles. She covered her arms with the skin of the forelegs. She cut off the skin that hung below the knees, and afterward used it to make a pair of leggings.

When the garment was fitted, Antler took it off. Then the women sat down and worked until it was done. They punched holes through the edges with a bone awl. Then they threaded the sinew through the holes in an "over-and-over seam."

" When the men saw the new garment, they wondered how it was made."

When the men saw the new garment, they wondered how it was made. So Antler and Birdcatcher showed them how it was done, and helped them to make warm garments of their own.

And so all the Cave-men soon had warm garments of fur. Sometimes they fastened them with buckles, and sometimes they used bone pins. They made long leggings of soft skins, and moccasins for their feet.

Perhaps you can think how they learned to make mittens and gloves. We know that they had warm mittens and gloves, for we have found pictures they made of them. When they dressed in their warm fur garments, the Cave-men did not fear the cold. If they wanted food, they put on their garments and went wherever they pleased.

A Cave-man's glove.

THINGS TO DO

If you can get a small skin, fit it to a doll the way you think the Cave-men fitted skins to their bodies. If you cannot get a skin, cut a piece of cloth so as to make it the shape of a skin, and show how the new suit was made.

Find as many things as you can that you can use for pins, buttons, and buckles.

Find as many ways as you can of sewing a simple seam. When you go to a museum notice how the seams are sewed. Why do you think people invented new stitches? Visit a shoemaker and notice how he sews.

Draw one of these pictures:—

The cold wind drives Fleetfoot into the cave.

Playing "Cave-bear."

XVII

THINGS TO THINK ABOUT

How do you think the children played in the winter? What do you play in the winter?

How do you think the Cave-men would hunt when there was only a light fall of snow?

How would they hunt when the snow was deep?

How would they hunt when there was a hard crust on the snow?

How the Children Played in Winter

When the children saw their fathers and mothers go out of doors, they, too, wanted to go. But they had no warm clothing, so their mothers tried to keep them in doors.

Sometimes Fleetfoot and Flaker teased to go out and play in the snow. And when the days were warm enough, Antler let them go out and play. But on very cold days they had to stay in the cave.

The children had good times in the cave. They played many animal games. They played they were grown men and women, and they made believe do all sorts of work. They peeked out of the cave many times each day. They heard their fathers and mothers talk. And they listened to Greybeard's stories.

And so the children always knew what the men and women were doing. After a heavy fall of snow, they knew they would trap the animals in the drifts. When a hard crust formed, they knew they would dig pitfalls.

6

Antler often wished that the children might play out doors every day. Greybeard wanted the boys to learn to make pitfalls and traps. But neither Antler nor Greybeard had thought of making clothing for little children.

The day Antler thought of making clothes for the boys, was the day they ran away to the pitfall. It was soon after Chipper came to the cave and said that two reindeer were in the pit.

When the boys heard what Chipper said, they were playing they were Bighorn and Chipper. They had tied the skins of wolves' heads over their heads, and they let the rest of the skins hang down as if they were capes.

When the news came about the reindeer, everybody was excited. Everybody hurried to the pitfall so as to see the reindeer. Nobody noticed the boys steal out of the cave. Nobody noticed them run to the pitfall.

But soon after she started, Antler saw the tracks of their bare feet. She guessed at once where the boys had gone. And it was then that she thought of making them clothing.

While the children slept that night, Antler talked with the women. And when morning came, the women took skins and made the children warm clothes and moccasins.

When the children put on their wolf-skin suits, they looked like a pack of wolves. Sometimes they played they were wolves. Then they chased make-believe wild horses.

Sometimes when the children were playing in the

snow, they found the antlers of a full-grown stag. The children began to look for the antlers of the full-grown stags in early winter. But they knew that the other reindeer kept their antlers until early spring.

An old stag's antlers were large and strong, and the children liked to find them. They would pick them up and hold them in their hands and would then make believe they were Cave-men trapping reindeer in the snow.

One day Greybeard showed Fleetfoot and Flaker how to trap the reindeer in the snow. He showed them how to dig a pitfall in the drifts. The boys found a large drift near the trail and they cut out a large block of snow. They hollowed a deep pit under the crust which they took pains not to break. Then they fitted the block of snow in its place, thus covering the pit.

To make sure that the reindeer would come to the pitfall they scattered moss over the thin crust. Then Greybeard taught them to say,

> *" Come down to the river, reindeer;*
> *Come down to the river to drink.*
> *Come eat the moss I have spread for you,*
> *Come and fall into my trap."*

All the Cave-men believed that these words would charm the reindeer to the spot. They always muttered such lines as charms when they went out to hunt. And so Greybeard taught the boys the lines, for he wanted them to know all the Cave-men's charms.

THINGS TO DO

Name the animals which you know by their tracks.　Draw a picture of the tracks you know best.

Tell a story about hunting an animal by tracking it.

Next time there is a heavy fall of snow, play hunting animals by driving them into the drifts.

See if you can show in your sand-box how the pitfall was made.

See if you can think of a way of having real drifts in your sand-box.

Draw a picture of the children playing with the antlers of the reindeer.

Draw a picture of the reindeer in the pitfall.

XVIII

THINGS TO THINK ABOUT

Do you know whether we can tell what the weather is going to be?

Have you ever heard any one talking about the signs of the weather?　What signs do you know?

Notice animals and see how they act before a storm.

Notice what animals and birds are here in summer that are not here in winter.　Are any here in winter that are not here in the summer?

Why did the bison go away from the Cave-men's hunting grounds each winter?　When they went away would they go in large or small herds?

If the weather kept pleasant how do you think they would travel?　What would they do if it looked like a storm?

Notice the animals that live near you and see whether they turn their heads or backs toward the storm.

Overtaken by a Storm

Winter passed and summer came and now it was almost gone.　The cattle had gone to the forests in the lowlands where they spent the winter. Straggling lines of bison were moving down the valley. Now and then they stopped a few days to eat the tall grass. Then they slowly moved onward toward the lower lands.

The days were like the Indian summer days which we sometimes have in late autumn. Everybody enjoyed each day as it came, and thought little about the coming cold. But one morning the sky was gray and gloomy, and the sun could not pierce through the heavy clouds. The air was cold and now and then a snowflake was falling.

There was no meat at the cave, and everybody was hungry. So Bighorn said to the men, "Let's hunt the bison to-day."

The men crowded around, for they were always glad to go hunting with Bighorn. As soon as he had shown them his plan, they took their weapons and started toward the herd.

Bighorn expected to find the herd feeding quietly on a hillside. But, instead, the bison were tossing their horns, sniffing the air, and looking this way and that.

Bighorn saw that the bison were restless and that he could not take them by surprise. "We shall have a hard chase," said he to the men, "if we get a bison to-day."

The men stood still for a moment, for they did not know what to do. Fine snowflakes were now falling and the dark clouds threatened a heavy storm. But the men were hungry and they were not ready to give up the hunt at once.

"Listen!" said Bighorn, as a low rumbling sound came from the upper valley.

The Cave-men put their ears to the ground and heard a sound like distant thunder. As they listened it came nearer and nearer and the ground seemed to shake.

The Cave-men were not afraid. They knew what the sound meant. The bison, too, knew what it meant They knew that winter was coming, and that it was time for them to be gone. They knew that the laggard herds were racing with the storm.

And so the sentinels of the scattered herds gave sig-nals to the bison. And before the Cave-men were on their feet, the bison had started toward the ford.

Louder and louder the rumbling sound grew as the great herd galloped on. The snow was now falling thick and fast, and a cold northwest wind was blowing. But in spite of the wind and the snow, the Cave-men pressed on toward the ford. Bighorn still hoped to get a bison as the great herd passed.

By the time the herd reached the ford, the wind had become a strong gale. The air was so thick with the snow that it nearly blinded the men. Then Bighorn turned and said to the men, "We must find a shelter from the storm."

The bison, too, tried to find a shelter. Some of them hugged up closely to the sheltered side of the cliffs. Others sought cover in the ravines. But many could find no protection, so they turned about and faced the storm.

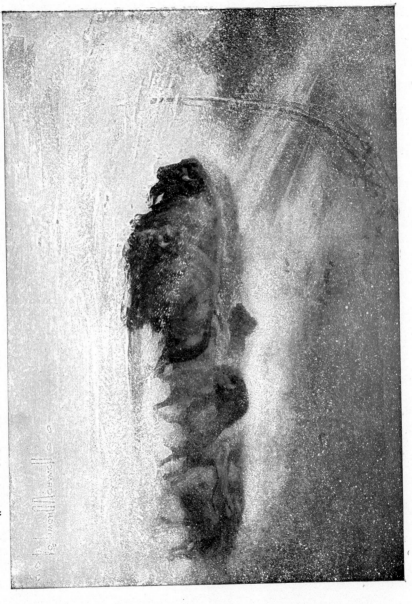

"*But many could find no protection, so they turned about and faced the storm.*"

The Cave-men wished they were safe at home, but they dared not go through the storm. They huddled together and felt their way to a spot where the snow did not drift. There they lay down in the snow and waited for the storm to cease.

THINGS TO DO

Name some bird that migrates. Tell all that you know about the way it migrates.

When you go out to play, show how the bison migrated in warm weather. Show how they migrated in cold weather.

Show in your sand-box where the deep drifts would be. Show places where the snow would not drift. If you cannot be sure about where the drifts would be, see if you can find out by watching the storms during winter.

If the Cave-men are buried in the snow, how do you think they can get air to breathe? How can they tell when the storm is over?

XIX

THINGS TO THINK ABOUT

What do you think those who stayed in the cave will do during the storm? Can you think of any way by which they could get food?

Did you ever walk on snow-shoes? How do you think people came to make snow-shoes?

How Antler Happened to Invent Snowshoes

Antler saw the coming storm and at once she thought of the fire. She called to the women. And soon they were all breaking branches with stone axes and mauls. The children piled the fagots together and carried them to the cave.

The snow was falling fast before they finished their work. They watched the storm for a little while and then went into the cave.

The children were hungry and asked for meat. But there was no meat in the cave. Antler tried to get the children to play and to forget that they were hungry. And the children played for a little while, but they soon grew tired. And so Antler gathered the children together and began to tell them stories.

As the storm raged fiercer and fiercer, Antler told stories of other storms. She had braved many storms on the wooded hills and the children liked to hear her stories.

A stone maul.

Among the stories she told that day was the story of the Big Bear. She said that the Big Bear lived in a cavern away up in the mountain. She said that he kept watch of the game and that sometimes he shut the game in his cavern. Antler said she had often heard the Big Bear above the voice of the storm. And Fleetfoot, listening for his voice, thought he heard it in the wailing of the storm.

In spite of the stories Antler told, the day was long and dreary. The next day was still more dreary, for the children were crying for food. Toward the close of day they were very tired, and soon they fell asleep.

Most of the women slept that night, but there was no sleep for Antler. She could not sleep when the children were hungry and when the men were out in

the storm. She stayed awake and watched and listened all through the long dark night.

Fur gloves.

Toward morning the storm began
to slacken, and Antler gave a sigh of
relief. She felt sure that many bison
were floundering in the drifts. She
hoped they were not far away from
the cave. So she dressed in her fur
garments and took a large knife and
an ax. And at break of day she set
out hoping to find a bison.

But the snow was very deep and
Antler could scarcely walk. She was faint from hunger
and cold. For a while she struggled through the drifts,
but soon her strength failed, and she sank down in the
snow.

As Antler lay in the deep drifts, she seemed power-
less to move. The thought of the hungry children,
however, made her turn to the gods. Then the branches
of spruce trees seemed to urge her on.

And so Antler took courage and grasping a strong
branch of a friendly spruce struggled through the deep
snow. She stepped upon the partly buried branches
and they helped her on her way.

A bison, floundering in a drift, filled her heart with
hope. But when she started toward the bison, Antler
sank down once more into the drifts. So again she
turned to the friendly trees, and again she reached out
to them for aid. And she broke branches from the
trees and bound them to her feet.

Starting once more, Antler walked as if on winged feet. She ran over the deep drifts. And since she could hunt as well as the men, she soon had plenty of meat.

As Antler was strapping her load upon her back, she heard a familiar voice. Quickly she turned, and her heart beat fast as she listened to hear it again. And seeing the men struggling through the drifts, she knelt and gave thanks to the gods.

Soon Antler arose and laid down her load; and breaking a handful of branches, she hurried over the drifts and met the Cave-men.

When the men saw Antler gliding over the drifts they wondered if it was one of the gods. Not until Antler spoke were they really sure it was she. And not until she showed them how to tie the branches to their feet did they understand what she had done. And even then they did not know that Antler had invented the snowshoe. Many people worked upon snowshoes before fine snowshoes were made. For when people heard what Antler had done, they tried different ways for themselves.

Of course all the people were glad when Antler returned with the men. They feasted and told stories all day long. And afterward the children played they were hunters overtaken by a storm, and they made little snowshoes and learned to walk over the drifts.

A snowshoe.

THINGS TO DO

The next time there is a storm listen to it and see if you can hear what the Cave-men thought was the voice of the Big Bear.   See if you can tell what it is that makes the music of the storm.

Listen to the music of the birds and see if you can give their songs and calls.

What other animals do you hear calling one another?   See if you can give their calls.

Tell a story of some storm you have seen.

Draw one of these pictures :—

Antler praying to the gods for help.

A bison floundering in the drift.

Antler bringing aid to the men.

Find a picture of a snowshoe, and tell how you think it was made.

Find something which you can use for making snowshoes.   Make a pair, and use them when you have a chance.

See if you can find out why the snowshoe keeps one from sinking in the snow.

XX

THINGS TO THINK ABOUT

Why would the women be apt to make traps before the men did? What animals did the men hunt most?   How did they hunt them? What animals did the women hunt most?   How?

How many kinds of knots can you tie?   Which of these knots slip? Which of these knots would be the best to use in a trap?

How Antler made Snares

While Fleetfoot and Flaker were little boys, they learned a few lessons in trapping.   The men seldom trapped at that time, but the women trapped in several ways.

Antler was only a little girl when she learned to catch birds with a seed on a string. She was called Snowflake then and she lived in another cave.

Snowflake's mother taught her to do all the things that little girls needed to know. She learned to hunt for roots and berries, to catch birds, and to make traps, besides learning to make tents, to prepare skins, and to make them into garments. It would take too long to tell all the things that little girls learned in those days.

Snowflake learned her lessons well and she found new ways of doing things. It was when she found a reindeer caught in the vines that she took the first step in making a snare. She had started to the hillside to dig roots and had gone only a little way when she heard something pulling and tugging among the vines.

She peeked through the branches to see what it was, and there stood a beautiful reindeer. His antlers were caught in the tangled vines and he was trying to get loose.

Snowflake's heart went pit-a-pat, pit-a-pat, when she saw the reindeer. But she kept going nearer, and the reindeer pulled and pulled until he was strangled by the vines.

When Snowflake came to the cave dragging the handsome reindeer, the people shouted for joy. And when they had knocked off the beautiful antlers, they gave them to Snowflake and changed her name.

Whenever she went to the spot where the reindeer was caught she always looked for another reindeer. But the reindeer kept away from the spot.

So, at length, Antler thought of cutting vines and fastening them to branches. Then she learned to tie knots that would slip and tighten when pulled. And, after a while, she used the slipknots in making many kinds of snares.

Antler watched the birds until she knew the spots where they liked to alight. Then she set snares on the ground and fastened them to strong branches.

The birds, alighting on the spot, caught their feet in the snare. When they tried to fly away, they pulled the slipknot which held them fast.

Some of the birds were frightened away, and did not return to the spot. So Antler tried to coax them back by scattering seeds near the snare.

" Then she set snares on the ground and fastened them to strong branches."

Once Antler set a snare in a rabbit path just high enough to catch the rabbit's head. A rabbit was caught, but he nibbled the cord and ran off with the snare. And so Antler learned to protect the cord by running it through a hollow bone.

There was no better trapper than Antler among all the Cave-men. It was she who taught the boys and girls how to make and set traps. When the marmots awoke from their long winter's sleep, all the children learned to catch them in traps. They learned to loosen the bark of a tree without breaking

"Antler learned to protect the cord by running it through a hollow bone."

it except along one edge. They used the bark as a leadway to a trap which they set near a marmot's hole. After placing the noose inside the bark, they fastened it to a bent sapling.

When the children went to the trap, they clapped

" *So it ran along and nibbled the bait until its sharp teeth cut the cord.*"

their hands and shouted. Then they took the marmot out of the trap and carried it to the cave. And they made a great noise when Bighorn said, "You will soon be very good trappers."

Then the children wanted to catch another marmot, so Antler went with them and showed them how the trap worked. The marmot coming out of his hole smelled the bait on the string. So it ran along and nibbled the bait until its sharp teeth cut the cord. Then the sapling sprang up and jerked the snare upward. And the weight of the marmot, pulling downward, drew the slipknot tight.

THINGS TO DO

Tie a slipknot at one end of a string, and show how to set it for snaring birds. Show how to set it for snaring rabbits. Find a hollow stick or a bone to protect the snare from the rabbit's teeth. Show how the marmot trap was set

Tell how you catch mice. Tell how you catch flies.

What animals do you know that sleep during the winter? How can they live so long without eating?

Draw one of these pictures:—

Snowflake finds a reindeer caught in the vines

Antler teaches the children to set traps.

Model a marmot in clay.

Name all the animals you know that burrow in the ground. Watch one of them and find out what it does.

XXI

THINGS TO THINK ABOUT

Why would the Cave-men be apt to lose many spears and javelins? How could they keep from losing the shafts?

Can you think of how they might find a way of saving their spearheads?

Find a picture of a barbed spearhead. Why did people begin to make barbs?

How Spears were Changed into Harpoons

None of the clans could make better weapons than the men of the Bison clan. Since boyhood, Greybeard had been known for his delicate spear points and knives. No workshop in all the valley was better known than his. But even Greybeard's weapons sometimes were known to fail. Even his spear points sometimes were lost in the chase.

For several days the men were at home making new weapons. They never made spears and javelins with sharper and finer points. They never made straighter and smoother shafts. When they started out to hunt, they were proud of their new weapons. All the Cavemen expected that before the day passed, they would have new trophies and fresh meat.

The women, trapping birds on the hillsides, listened from time to time. They expected to hear Bighorn's whistle when the animals were ready to be skinned. But the day passed, and no signal came.

At sunset the men returned, but they were gloomy and silent. They brought no trophies, and they spoke not a word of the chase.

No wonder the men were gloomy and silent. Their precious spears and javelins had been lost in the chase. It was not because the men were careless. It was not because they were not skillful in making spears and javelins. It was because these weapons, when thrown from the hand, could not strike deadly blows.

7

The Cave-men had thrown at the wild horses with a sure aim. Their javelins and spears went right to the mark. When the horses ran, the Cave-men followed. But in spite of all they could do, the wild horses were soon out of sight.

Some of the horses received ugly wounds and carried the weapons far away. Others received slight wounds, they brushed off the spears and javelins, which fell and were lost in the tall grass.

Time and again, hunted animals had escaped with only a wound. Wounded animals had often escaped with a spear or javelin. But never before had so many animals escaped with so many precious weapons.

Of course there was nothing for the Cave-men to do but to make new weapons. But it took a long time to season the sticks for straight and smooth shafts. It took patience and skill for the Cave-men to make delicate flint points. Perhaps this was why the Cave-men learned to retrieve the weapons they threw.

A chisel-scraper.

Ever since the Cave-men had learned to make spears, they had lashed the head to the shaft. They thought that this was the only way to make a good spear. Chipper was the first Cave-man who invented a new way.

Chipper was all alone in the workshop. He had finished a spear point which he held in his hand. Without thinking what he was doing, he slipped the tang into a hollow reed which he picked up from the ground.   If it had not been for a hungry wolf, he might have thought no more about it.

But the wolf had smelled the meat which was on the ground close to the workshop.   Hearing a sound, Chipper looked just in time to see the wolf spring toward the meat.

The spear flew from Chipper's hand before he stopped to think.   And Chipper sprang upon the wolf and engaged in a hand-to-hand fight.

At the first sound of the combat the Cave-men rushed to the spot.   There they found that Chipper had already secured his prize.

While the Cave-men looked at the wolf, Chipper told them what had happened.   He showed them the reed which he had used in hurling his new spear point. The men looked at the hollow reed and tried it to see how it worked.   Other reeds were on the ground.   So the men fitted spearheads into the reeds and practiced throwing that way.   They played with the reeds the rest of the day.

When they worked at their weapons again, Chipper, alone, tried a new way.   He made a loose shaft with a socket in the end.   During the next chase they lost many weapons.   Chipper lost many spearheads; but he always found his loose shaft.

When the Cave-men noticed that Chipper never lost his shaft they began to make loose shafts.   And they got the idea of a barbed spearhead from a wound which was made by a broken point.   They found such a point deep down in

A barbed point.

the wound of a bison.   The sharp edge had caught in the bison's flesh.   And every movement of the bison had driven the spearhead deeper.

It was by paying attention to such little things that the Cave-men learned to make barbed spears.   When the Cave-men learned that barbed spearheads made very dangerous wounds, they were willing to take the trouble of making the barbed points.

But no Cave-man was willing to lose one of his barbed spear points.   Perhaps that is why the men began to tie the barbed heads to the loose shaft.   When they first did this, they did not know that their spears had become harpoons.

A harpoon.

THINGS TO DO

Find a hollow reed and use it for a shaft.   Make a shaft with a socket in it.   Fit a spearhead into the socket.   Change the spear so as to make a harpoon.

Draw a picture of the chase of the wild horses.

Think of a wild horse running very fast.   See if you can model a wild horse in clay so as to show that it has great speed.

XXII

THINGS TO THINK ABOUT

Why was the harpoon a better weapon for hunting than the spear or javelin?   What could hunters do to keep smooth shafts from slipping from their hands?   What is the harpoon used for to-day?

Why do animals become more cunning after they are hunted?

How the Cave-men Hunted with Harpoons

Once again the Cave-men went out to hunt the wild horses. Once again they took new weapons. But instead of spears and javelins they carried barbed harpoons.

From a high hill they saw the horses on the edge of a grassy upland. They hurried over the wooded hills and crept through the tall grass. When Bighorn gave the signal the sentinels pricked up their ears. But before they could give the alarm, the men had thrown their harpoons.

The frightened horses crowded upon one another. Snapping sounds of breaking shafts, sharp cries of wounded horses, and loud shouts of Cave-men added to their terror.

The snorting of the sentinels warned the Cave-men back. A signal from the leader brought order to the herd. It began to move as though it were one solid mass.

Away the herd galloped, striking terror to all creatures in the way. But the wounded horses soon lagged. In vain they tried to keep up. At each step the shaft of the harpoon swung under their feet. At each step the barbed head pierced deeper and deeper. So the Cave-men had little trouble in finishing the chase.

Perhaps you think the Cave-men had no trouble in hunting after that. They had less trouble for some time, and they all prized their harpoons. But on cold days, when their hands were stiff, the smooth shafts slipped from their grasp.

When they used shafts with knobs and large joints, it was easy to keep a firm hold. So the men made shafts with larger knobs and they put girdles around the smooth shafts.

At their games of throwing spears and javelins, Bighorn was almost sure to win. It was partly because he had large hands and very strong fingers. By bending one finger like   a hook and striking the butt of

the shaft, he could send a harpoon straight to the mark.

Chipper's hands were not very large. His fingers were not so strong as Bighorn's. But Chipper was a bright young man, and he found a way of using a spear-noose so that he could throw as well as Bighorn.

The spear-noose was a simple thing. Chipper made it by tying a noose in each end of a cord. When he used it, he slipped one noose

Chipper using a spear-noose.

around his thumb and the other around one finger. Then he grasped the spear near the butt and slipped the cord around the knob.   The spear-noose was a great help to hunters whose hands were not large and strong.

Every time the Cave-men made new weapons, they worked very well for a short time.   But as soon as the animals learned about them, they became more cunning in getting away.   Wild horses kept sentinels on knolls and hilltops so that they could see an enemy from afar.   They guarded their herds so carefully that the Cave-men could scarcely get near enough to hit them with their harpoons.

And so the Cave-men returned many times bearing no trophies.   They returned many times giving no signal for the women to come for fresh meat.

THINGS TO DO

Take a harpoon and show how the shaft would swing against the feet of an animal that had been hit by the head.

Make a girdle around a smooth shaft, or make a shaft with a knob or large joint near the butt.

Make a spear-noose and show how Chipper used it.

Think of the wild horses during the first few minutes after the men threw their harpoons.   See if you can draw a picture of them.

XXIII

THINGS TO THINK ABOUT

Think of as many hard things as you can that the Cave-men had to do.

Why did they have to do these things?   What kind of men did the Cave-men have to be?

Think of as many ways as you can that the Cave-men would use to teach the boys.   What tests do you think they would give the boys?

"*And so the Cave-men tested the boys in many different ways.*"

How the Cave-men Tested Fleetfoot and Flaker

Winters came and went, and Fleetfoot and Flaker grew to be large boys. They watched the men; they heard them talk; they learned what a Cave-man had to do.

Greybeard told them stories of brave hunters that lived long ago. He told them about the animals they must learn to hunt. The boys listened to the stories. And they thought there was no animal too fierce for them to fight. They thought there was no river too swift for them to cross. They thought there was no mountain too steep for them to climb.

But the boys had not learned how fierce a bison can be. They had never crossed a raging river nor climbed a mountain peak.

The men knew that the boys needed to try their strength before they could be really strong. They knew they must do brave deeds before they could be really brave. They knew they must suffer patiently before they could have self-control. And so the Cave-men tested the boys in many different ways.

If the boys stood the tests, the Cave-men shouted praises; but if they showed any sign of fear, the Cave-men jeered at them.

Sometimes the boys were given nothing to eat until they brought food from the hunt. And even then they were not always allowed to touch the food which was near. When the boys were fasting, the Cave-men tempted them with food. And if the boys took even a bite, they failed in the test. So Fleetfoot and Flaker learned to fast without a word of complaint.

One of the hardest things which the boys had to do was to make their own weapons. At first, Greybeard helped them; but, later, they had to do their own work.

So the boys learned to go to the trees that had the best wood for shafts. They learned to cut, and peel, and scrape, and oil, and season, and polish the sticks before they were ready to use. No wonder the boys became tired before all this work was done.

Then they worked very carefully before they could make good spearheads. They hunted for the best stones and learned to shape them very well. When they forgot and struck hard blows, they spoiled the flint points. Then Greybeard would tell them that the strongest and bravest hunters were those who could strike the gentlest blows.

It was work of this kind that was harder for the boys than chasing a wild horse or a reindeer. If they had not known that they must have weapons, they would not have had patience to do it.

While the boys worked at their weapons, they thought of what they would do with them. They thought of the trophies they would bring home and what the people would say. And they learned to sing at their work and to mark the time for each blow. And so they managed to keep at work until the weapons were done.

One day when the boys were flaking spear points, Fleetfoot turned to Flaker and said, "Do you know who made the first flaker?"

"Yes," answered Flaker, "it was Greybeard."

"No, no!" said Fleetfoot, "Nimble-finger did it."

Greybeard heard Fleetfoot speak his name and he came to the spot. Then it was that Fleetfoot learned that Greybeard was Nimble-finger.

After that Fleetfoot took great pains to learn how to flake flint points. He watched Greybeard as he worked and he listened to all he said.

Before many years had passed, the boys could make good weapons. They knew every spot on their own hunting ground. They knew the wild animals that lived there and what they liked to do They knew each animal by its track. Each sound of the woods, each patch of light, they learned to read as you read a book.

THINGS TO DO

Name things you will have to learn before you are full-grown.

What kind of tests do you have to take?

Tell a story of the way the Cave-men tested Fleetfoot and Flaker.

Tell a story of all that you think happened the day that Fleetfoot learned that Greybeard was Nimble-finger.

Name the birds you can tell by their song. Name those you can tell by sight.

Draw one of these pictures:—

Testing Fleetfoot and Flaker.

Fleetfoot and Flaker in the workshop.

Fleetfoot discovers Nimble-finger

"Then their antlers crashed in a swift charge"

XXIV

THINGS TO THINK ABOUT

What animals would the Cave-men see just before winter? Which of these live in herds? How are the leaders of the herds chosen?
What kind of a voice does the reindeer have when it is good-natured?
What kind of a voice does it have when it is angry?

Fleetfoot and Flaker see a Combat

One day just before winter, Fleetfoot and Flaker went out on the hills. The reindeer were coming back and the boys wanted to see them.

They had gone only a little way, when they saw two handsome stags. Each wanted to be leader of the reindeer herd, and so they were trying their strength.

The stags stood head to head, their red eyes blazing like fire. Their hair stood on end. They stamped their hoofs on the hard ground. They hissed fierce blasts to and fro.

Slowly and carefully they changed their position, still keeping head to head. Each reindeer knew that the lances of the other could strike deadly blows. Each reindeer had fought too many battles to expose himself to such blows.

And so the stags eyed each other, getting more angry all the while. Louder and fiercer sounded their blasts. Then their antlers crashed in a swift charge.

They pulled and pushed with all their might in a life and death struggle. Not until their strength was exhausted did they stop a moment to rest.

Then they tried to draw apart, but they found they could not do it. Each stag was held a prisoner by the antlers of the other. In vain the handsome creatures pulled and pushed. Each was held fast. And the boys, seeing their chance, secured both of the reindeer.

Perhaps it was well for the reindeer that the boys were there. At least, the boys saved them from a more horrible death. Reindeer caught in this way have suffered from hunger and thirst many days before death came.

The boys admired the beautiful reindeer as they lay stretched out on the ground. They felt of their polished antlers that had dealt many powerful blows. And they wished they had such weapons as these to use all of the time.

THINGS TO DO

Show how the reindeer stood in the combat and how they changed their positions. Draw the picture.

Take a flat surface of clay and see if you can model a reindeer so that it will stand out a little from the surface.

Tell a story of what you think happened at the cave after the boys killed the reindeer.

XXV

THINGS TO THINK ABOUT

If you have ever seen a cat hunt, tell how she does it. Can you think why cats do not hunt together?

Do dogs hunt alone, or with one another? How do wolves hunt?

In what ways can animals help one another in hunting? What animals do wolves hunt to-day? What animals did the wolves hunt in the time of the Cave-men?

What Happened when Fleetfoot and Flaker Hunted the Bison

When summer came, Fleetfoot and Flaker watched the bison from day to day. The wolves, too, watched the bison. One day the boys saw two wolves hunt a bison that had strayed from the herd.

The wolves walked boldly up toward the bison until they were only a few paces away. Then they went cautiously.

The bison paid no attention at first; but when the wolves came closer, he stamped his foot and shook his horns. Any animal could know that the bison meant, "It is dangerous here. Keep away!"

But the wolves had a plan and they carried it out. The smaller wolf kept the bison's attention by making believe attack from the front. This gave the big wolf a chance; and he cut the large muscles of the bison's knees with his sharp teeth. The bison was thus crippled so badly that the wolves were more than a match for him.

"I wonder if we could get a bison," said Flaker as the boys watched the wolves at their feast.

"Let's try," said Fleetfoot.

"But how can we get close up," said Flaker, "without frightening the bison away?"

"Let's dress in wolf-skins," said Fleetfoot, "and make believe we are wolves."

And the boys dressed in wolf-skins and took their
best hunting knives. They watched the herd until
they saw a large bison stray away. Then the boys
approached the bison, and they looked so much like
wolves that they got very close before the bison threatened with his horns.

Then the boys made the attack. Flaker took the
part of the little wolf and attacked the bison's head.
Fleetfoot took the part of the big wolf and tried to
cripple the bison.

But the boys had not counted upon the bison's tough
skin. They had not counted upon his muscles, which
were as hard as boards. Flaker's dagger glanced off at
one side and merely scratched the bison. But it made
the creature so angry that he charged upon Flaker.

Meanwhile Fleetfoot was doing his best to cut the
hard muscles of the bison's knee. He forgot about
everything else until he had lamed one of the forelegs.
It was then that the bison charged and that Flaker
called for help. And then Fleetfoot tried to rescue
Flaker by drawing the bison's attention away.

Fleetfoot did this just in time to save Flaker's life.
He struck at the Bison's head, then dodged in time to
escape his horns. He dodged again and again until he
was almost exhausted. The bison limped, but he
seemed as strong and as furious as ever Once again
the bison charged, and again Fleetfoot dodged. Then
a spear whizzed past Fleetfoot's head and a voice
called, "Climb a tree."

Fleetfoot never remembered running to the tree.

"*They looked so much like wolves that they got very close before the bison threatened.*"

He never remembered climbing it. But for many days he seemed to see himself in the tree and the bison just beneath. For many days he seemed to hear Greybeard's welcome voice.

Greybeard and Fleetfoot stayed in the trees until the bison started up the ravine. Then they climbed down from one of the trees and hurried to see what had happened to Flaker.

A Cave-man's carving of a "hamstrung" animal.

THINGS TO DO

Tell something that you have learned from watching an animal.

Mention as many things as you can that you think the Cave-men learned from animals.

Straighten and bend your elbow or knee so as to find where the strong muscles are.

Tell why the Cave-men tried to cut the strong muscles of the bison's knee. We say when we cut these large muscles that we have "hamstrung" the animal.

Look at the picture of a Cave-man's carving of an animal which has been "hamstrung." Can you tell what animal it is?

Think of the two wolves coming up toward the bison. Model one of them in clay. See if the children can guess which one it is.

XXVI

THINGS TO THINK ABOUT

What do you think had happened to Flaker? If any of his bones were broken, do you think the Cave-men could set them? Do you think there were doctors when the Cave-men lived? Who would do the work which doctors do to-day?

What the Cave-men did for Flaker

Fleetfoot ran ahead of Greybeard and found Flaker on the ground. Fleetfoot stooped and looked into his face. He called him by name. No answer came. Then Fleetfoot asked Greybeard if Flaker was dead.

Greybeard shook his head as he bent down and laid his hands upon the boy. He examined his wounds, then said to Fleetfoot, "Let's carry him down to the cool spring."

So Greybeard and Fleetfoot lifted Flaker and carried him gently down to the spring. There they bathed his face and the ugly wounds with fresh cool water. They bound his wounds with strips of the skins that the boys wore that day.

When Greybeard tried to set the broken bones, Flaker began to moan. He opened his eyes for a moment; then he fell back in a swoon.

Then Greybeard sent Fleetfoot to the cave for help. And Fleetfoot hurried and told Antler; and Antler, picking up some little things which she knew she would need, and telling the women to follow quickly with a large skin, went with Fleetfoot to the spot where Flaker lay.

Greybeard was watching beside the boy when Antler arrived. He helped her set the broken bones and then they prepared to carry him home.

Taking the skin which the women brought, Antler stretched it upon the ground. Then the women helped

What the Cave-men did for Flaker.

her lift the boy and lay him upon the skin. Gently they laid him upon the stretcher. Softly they stepped as they carried him home. They tended him carefully many days

Flaker's wounds soon healed. But when he was strong enough to walk, the Cave-men saw that he was lame.

Flaker was always lame after that. The bones had slipped out of place and now it was too late to reset them. Afterwards the Cave-men learned better ways of setting broken bones. They found better ways of holding them in place while they grew together.

Perhaps the Cave-men learned this by watching the wild animals. Some birds, when they break a leg, hold the bones in place with wet clay. Sometimes we use a plaster cast, but the Cave-men knew nothing about such a way.

The days seemed long to Flaker while he was getting well. Everybody was kind to him, but it seemed hard to keep quiet when everybody else was moving about.

When Fleetfoot went out to hunt, Flaker wanted to go too. But he could not go, and so Fleetfoot used to tell him everything that happened.

THINGS TO DO

Show how the women helped Antler put Flaker upon the skin. Show how they carried him home. Draw one of the pictures.

Find out why a child's bones will grow together more easily than an old person's bones. See if you can find out what bones are made of. Soak a bone in acid and see what happens to it. Burn a bone and see what

happens to it.   Why do a child's bones break less easily than an old person's?

If there is a spring in your neighborhood, go and see it.   Find out where the water comes from.

XXVII

THINGS TO THINK ABOUT

If Flaker is lame, how will he be able to get food? What do you think he can do that will be useful to the clan?

Do you think the Cave-men took as good care of the sick, and the lame, and the old people, as we do? What could they do for them?

Why did the men use weapons more than tools? Why did the women use tools more than weapons?

Think of as many tools as you can that the women used.

How Flaker Learned to Make Weapons of Bone

Before Flaker was hurt he and Fleetfoot had planned to do many things. But now Flaker was lame, and all the Cave-men knew he would never be able to hunt.

When Flaker first knew it, he was very sad. And so Fleetfoot tried to comfort him. Each day he brought him a bird or a rabbit, and he told him all that had happened.

For a while Flaker thought that if a man could not hunt, there was nothing else for him to do. But soon he found there were many things to do besides going out to hunt.

Flaker began by doing a few little things to help Fleetfoot. He helped him flake heads for harpoons and javelins and make strong shafts.

When Greybeard and Fleetfoot praised his work, Flaker was very happy. And so Flaker busied himself in the workshop when the men went out to hunt. Sometimes Chipper helped him, and often Greybeard worked with him.

When Flaker was tired he would look at the trophies which were fastened on the wall near the cave. He was always glad to see the locked antlers of the two stags.

As he looked at the strong antlers, he could almost see the handsome stags. He thought of them standing head to head ready to strike deadly blows. And he wished he had had such powerful weapons to meet the bison's charge.

The children wanted to be good to Flaker and so they brought him the antlers they found. They liked to play with the antlers, and their mothers used them in many ways. They had learned to cut them with choppers and chisels, and sometimes they cut them with stone knives.

All the women used the small prongs of the antlers. They used them as wedges in prying the bark loose from the sap-wood of young trees. All the women had learned to make hammers of antler by making two cuts near the base. And sometimes they used the broad end of the brow antler instead of a stone chisel.

Once when Flaker was watching Antler, he thought she was making a dagger. But Antler had not thought of making a dagger. She was

A wedge or tent pin.

making a hammer and wedge. When she had finished, she dropped the long beam of the antler upon the ground and went away with her tools.

Flaker kept his eyes fixed upon the long beam. The more he looked at it, the more it looked like a dagger. At length he reached and picked it up. Then he took his knife and began to cut it.

That night when Fleetfoot came home, Flaker gave him a dagger of reindeer horn. Fleetfoot showed it to Bighorn, who took it, then tossed it on the ground.

Bighorn had never seen such a dagger. He thought a good dagger had to be made of stone. So he made fun of Flaker's weapon, then thought no more about it.

But Greybeard and Chipper did not make fun of the weapons Flaker made. They tried the dagger next day, and found that it stood the test. So they asked Flaker to make each of them daggers and javelins of reindeer horn.

The head of a javelin.

THINGS TO DO

Tell all you know about the antlers of full-grown stags. Tell all you know about the antlers of other reindeer.

Look at the antlers in the pictures on pages 16, 17, 108, and 121. Find the part that would make such a wedge as is shown on page 119. Find the part that would make such a hammer as is shown on page 74. Find a part for a chisel or scraper Find the long beam that was used in making such a dagger as is shown on page 123. Do you think that Flaker's first dagger was carved in this way? Can you tell why the Cave-men carved their weapons?

Act out the part of this story you like best.
Draw one of these pictures :—
    Flaker watching for Fleetfoot's return.
    The children bringing antlers to Flaker.
    The women at work making tools.
    Fleetfoot showing the dagger to Bighorn.
    Greybeard and Chipper asking Flaker to make daggers.
Make as many simple tools as you can out of bone or horn. Find ways of using them.

XXVIII

THINGS TO THINK ABOUT

What do you think Flaker used in cutting the antler? What tools will he need to use in making weapons of bone or horn?

What do you think the first saws were? How do you think people came to use saws? How large do you think they were?

What are files used for? Can you think what the first files were like? What do you think they were used for?

How Flaker Invented the Saw

How glad Flaker was when Greybeard and Chipper asked him to make them some daggers! He looked at all the antlers the children had brought. He thought of the rein- deer he had seen with antlers such as these. He remembered the handsome reindeer with their deadly weapons, and at

A small antler.

length he chose the large antlers which had belonged to a handsome stag.

Flaker looked at the long beams and decided to use them for daggers. He took his knife to cut off the prongs, but he could scarcely cut them with a knife.

Flaker knew that the women cut the prongs with a chopper, but a chopper was a woman's tool. And Flaker wanted to be like the men. And so he kept working with his knife, but he wished he had taken a beam which the women had left.

When he was tired using his knife, he played with some flint flakes. He ran his fingers over the sharp edges. Then he carelessly pressed off tiny flakes.

But Flaker soon tired of this and he picked up the antler again. He pushed a flint flake back and forth upon one of the prongs of the antler.

Flaker was simply playing at first; but when he saw that the flint was cutting, his play became real work. And he kept on pushing and pulling the flake until the prong fell to the ground. Then he sawed off other prongs, but he did not know he was sawing.

Flaker had never seen a saw and he did not know what it was. He did not know that when he pressed off the tiny flakes he made the teeth of a flint saw.

But Flaker had made a saw. It was only the rough edge of a flint flake. No doubt such rough edges had been made many times before. But Flaker learned to use the rough edge by pushing and pulling it back and forth.

A knife with two blades, a saw, and a file, all in one.

When Flaker sawed the prongs from the beam, some of the places were rough. So he rubbed them with the face of the flint until he made them smooth. When Flaker did this, the flake, which had been only a knife, became a file as well as a saw.

Greybeard and Chipper tried the new daggers and found that they were sharp and strong. And the next time they went on the chase they took the new weapons along.

Bighorn saw the new weapons, but he said little about them. For Bighorn knew better than to make fun of weapons Greybeard used.

Nothing pleased Flaker more than to be able to help Greybeard. And so he cherished the new tool that he used in shaping reindeer horn. Sometimes he showed it to Greybeard, who was always kind to the boys. But even the wise old man had no idea of what a wonderful tool it was.

The other Cave-men saw the tool, but they thought very little about it. They cared a great deal about the weapons they used in the chase. But few of the Cave-men ever thought of making anything they did not need right away.

A Cave-man's dagger of carved antler.

And so little was said about the new tool which was a knife with two blades, a saw, and a file, all in one. Nobody dreamed at that time that the little tool was the forerunner of a great change.

THINGS TO DO

If you can strike off a large flint flake with three faces, see if you can make it into a knife-saw-file.

Look at the picture, or at the real tool you have made, and find the plain face that can be used as a file.

Find the two edges which can be used as knives. Find the edge which has a crest of teeth, and which can be used as a saw.

Draw one of these pictures :—

The women chopping prongs from the beam of the antler.

Flaker sawing the prongs off the antler.

XXIX

THINGS TO THINK ABOUT

Can you think why the females and the young males of the reindeer herd could drive the old stags away during the winter? Could they do it in the summer?

Why can the reindeer walk easily in the snow or on slippery places?

What is it that makes the clicking sound when reindeer walk or run?

Why were the Cave-men careful to make no mistake in the dance?

The Reindeer Dance

Fleetfoot did not hunt with the men, but he learned many things from them. In early winter, he heard them tell stories of dangerous encounters with ugly stags. When the old stags shed their antlers, he saw the men dance the reindeer dance.

Fleetfoot mimicked the reindeer's movements and the grunting sounds they made But he was not allowed to join with the men in dancing the reindeer dance. Only brave men were allowed to join in the dance. Only the bravest men were allowed to lead.

But Fleetfoot stood near and saw everything that was done. Some of the men put on headdresses made of the antlers of the reindeer. Others put on reindeer suits without the headdress of antlers. Those that were to be the Cave-men painted their faces and carried trophies.

A Cave-man's mortar stone for grinding paint.

Fleetfoot wished that he could have a headdress and take part in the dance. He wondered how long he would have to wait before he could dance with the men. He wondered how many brave things he must do before he would rank as a man.

And when Fleetfoot saw the men standing in silence while Greybeard made offerings to the gods, he looked at the brave old man and wondered how a man could be so wise. Then he thought of Chew-chew's stories of brave men of olden times.

At length Fleetfoot saw Flaker, who was sitting all alone. He went and sat beside him and they watched the men dance.

The men had finished dressing, and the women were seated on the ground. They had rolls of skin, and rude drums, and rattles of reindeer hoofs.

At a signal from Bighorn, a group of men came dancing to the music of the rattles. They moved about and made low grunting sounds as though they were a reindeer herd.

Then the music changed. The women drummed

upon skins and hummed in a weird way. They tried to show by the sound of the music the coming of a storm. At the first sound of the weird music, the reindeer pricked up their ears. Then the larger reindeer that had lost their antlers started off to make-believe higher lands. There they made believe paw the snow until they found the moss. As the music of the storm grew louder, the herd followed to the higher lands. And with many an angry threat they drove the old stags away.

A drum.

Then the drumming and humming became fainter, and at last the sounds died away. But still the faint clicking of the rattles marked each step of the men in the dance.

Another signal from Bighorn marked the change to a new scene. Trails were marked upon the ground and sticks placed for hills and streams.

While the reindeer pretended to feed, a group of Cave-men appeared. Bighorn, who was still the leader, sent Little-bear to watch where the trail crossed the hills. Chipper was sent to lie in wait at the spot where the trail crossed the river. And Bighorn, himself, took his stand at the point where the trails crossed.

When the men took their places, others crept back of the herd. Only the light music of the rattles sounded as the reindeer moved about.

As the men came nearer the reindeer herd, the sentinels showed signs of fear. The clicking of the rattles was quicker. The herd became thoroughly alarmed and the women shook the rattles and made a loud din.

Then the reindeer started on their old trails and came near the spots where the men were hid. The clicking of the rattles marked the time for the running, and the beating of the drum showed when javelins were hurled. Soon the shouts of the men and the rattles and drums made a loud noise.

All the Cave-men enjoyed the dance. They danced it without a mistake. And so they felt sure that the god of the reindeer would give them success in the chase.

THINGS TO DO

Model in your sand-box the spot where the reindeer dance was danced.

Model the trails where the Cave-men thought the reindeer would run when alarmed.

Make rattles of something which you can find, and show how to mark time with them.

If you can get a skin, see if you can stretch it over something so as to make a drum. Try different ways, and tell which is best.

Dramatize this lesson.

Draw a picture to illustrate it.

XXX

THINGS TO THINK ABOUT

Can you think why hunters frequently have famines? At what season of the year would they be most likely to have a famine?

Can you think why they did not preserve and save food in times of plenty?

If game should be scarce on a hunting ground, do you think all of the people could stay at home ? What do you think would happen at such a time ?

Have you ever heard that the Indians used to be afraid of having their pictures taken ? Why were they afraid of it ?

Fleetfoot Prepares for His Final Test

Toward the close of winter rumors of famine came to the Bison clan. Several times people came from neighboring clans and asked Antler for food. There was plenty of meat in the cave, so she gave to those who asked. The strangers soon went away, and the Bison clan forgot about them.

The next summer game was scarce on several of the old hunting grounds. There was not enough food for all. People began to wander away from their old homes. Small groups of men, women, and children, set out in different directions.

Game was still plenty on the lands of the Bison clan. When the neighbors knew this, they came to hunt on these lands. The day Fleetfoot went away to fast, strange people came and camped.

The next day the Bison clan drove them away. A few days later other strangers came, and they, too, were driven away. Bighorn was angry when the strangers first came, but soon he became alarmed.

Just as the men and women were holding a council to consider what to do, the strangers disappeared. Not until Fleetfoot returned did the Bison clan know who they were or why they came.

"People began to wander away from their old homes."

Before Fleetfoot went away to fast, he had been curious about the Big Bear. He had heard many stories about the Big Bear ever since he was a child. He had heard that the Big Bear guarded the game and kept the animals in the rocky cavern. He had wondered if he could climb the mountains and find the cave of the Big Bear.

Before Flaker was hurt, the boys had planned to go to the mountains. They had planned to make friends with the Big Bear and learn where he kept the game. They had planned to climb the highest peaks and see what there was beyond.

Once, when the boys asked Greybeard if they might go to the mountains, Greybeard said, "No, no, my children! Wait a while. You are not yet old enough to go."

And so the boys waited, but they still talked about going to the cavern of the Big Bear. After Flaker was hurt they still planned, but they planned for Fleetfoot to go alone.

One day when the boys were talking together, Greybeard came to Fleetfoot and said, "The time you have waited for has come. Prepare for your final test."

This was glad news for Fleetfoot. At last he was to have a chance to prove himself worthy to rank with the men. Flaker rejoiced with Fleetfoot, yet he could not help feeling sad.

The Bison clan had decided that Fleetfoot should go to a quiet spot. There he was to fast and pray until he received a sign from the gods. And when he had done their bidding, he was to return for his final test.   This test once passed, Fleetfoot would be counted one of the men.

Before Fleetfoot went, Greybeard instructed him in the use of prayers and charms.   Antler gave him a magic powder and showed him how to prepare it from herbs.   And the men told him of their tests, and the signs they received from the gods.

Flaker had listened to every word that Greybeard had said.   He had thought of all the dangers which Fleetfoot might encounter.   And he wondered if there was not a way to protect Fleetfoot from harm.

Flaker knew that the reindeer dance was a prayer of the Cave-men to their gods.   He knew each movement in the dance was to help the gods understand.   He felt sure that the gods would help Fleetfoot if he could make them understand.   And so he determined to make a prayer which Fleetfoot could carry with him.

Perhaps you will think that the prayer Flaker made was a very strange prayer.   But many people in all parts of the world have made such prayers.   It was a prayer to the Big Bear of the mountains.   Flaker scratched it upon a smooth pebble with a flint point.   It was a picture of the Big Bear, and Flaker made it so that Fleetfoot could control the actions of the Big Bear.

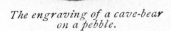

The engraving of a cave-bear on a pebble.

When Flaker gave the prayer to Fleetfoot he told him to guard it with great care. Fleetfoot took the prayer and promised to keep it near his side. Then the boys made an offering to the Big Bear and asked him to guide the way.

When at length Fleetfoot was ready to start, Greybeard spoke these parting words: "Forget not the offerings to the gods, and remember they must be made with true words and a faithful heart."

THINGS TO DO

Show in your sand-box where you think the mountains were. Model them and show that they were almost covered with snow. Show good places for neighboring hunting grounds.

Tell why game might be scarce in some hunting grounds and plenty in others.

Dramatize this story. Draw pictures which will show what happened. See if you can engrave some animal upon wood or soft stone.

XXXI

THINGS TO THINK ABOUT

Where do you think Fleetfoot will go while he is away from home? Find a picture of a glacier, and see if you can tell how a glacier is made. In what places does the snow stay all the year round? If a great deal of snow falls each year, what do you think will become of it? Find out whether there have ever been glaciers near where you live. If there have, see if you can find any traces of them.

Fleetfoot Fasts and Prays

None of the Cave-men knew where Fleetfoot would go to fast and pray. He scarcely knew himself, but all the time he kept thinking of the Big Bear of the Mountains. And so he turned his steps toward the high mountain peaks.

He followed the bison trail, for that was a sure guide. It led up the river a long way, and then skirted a dark forest. He crossed the river and went to the forest. There he sought out a lonely spot where he stayed several days.

As soon as he had made a fire, Fleetfoot made offerings to the gods. His offerings were fish he caught in the river and birds he caught in snares.

Although Fleetfoot offered meat to the gods, he did not taste it himself. When he was ready to sleep, he rubbed a pinch of wood-ashes upon his breast and prayed thus to the fire god: "O fire god, hover near me while I sleep. Hear my prayer. Grant good dreams to me this night. Grant me a sign that thou wilt aid me. Lead my feet in the right way."

The first night Fleetfoot had no dreams. The second night he dreamed he was a child again and that he lived in his old home. The third night he dreamed of the Big Bear of the Mountains. He thought that he climbed the mountain crags and went to the Big Bear's cave. He dreamed that the Big Bear spoke to him and asked him whence he came. Then strange people seemed to come out of the cave and wave their weapons in a threatening way. After that Fleetfoot remembered nothing except that the Big Bear seemed like a friend.

At daybreak Fleetfoot awoke, and at once he thought of his dream. He took the pebble from a little bag.

Then he made an offering to the bear as he spoke these words: "O Big Bear! O mighty hunter! Show me the way to thy caverns. Show me where thou keepest the game. Give me strength to meet all dangers. Fill my enemies with fear."

Then, remembering what Greybeard had said, Fleetfoot gave offerings to all the animals he hoped to kill. In this way he thought the gods would help him when he went out to hunt.

As soon as the offerings were made, Fleetfoot looked for a sign from the gods. The winds began to blow. Dark clouds began to climb the sky. Then the thunders pealed through the heavens.

Fleetfoot, faint from his long fast, took courage from these signs. The winds seemed to be messengers bearing his prayer to the gods. The dark clouds seemed to be the enemies he would meet on the way. The peals of thunder sounded to him like promises of strength. The bright lightning in the sky flashed a message of hope. A flock of swallows circling near seemed to point the way. And so Fleetfoot refreshed himself and started toward the mountains.

It would take too long to tell all the things that happened to Fleetfoot before he returned. One of the first things he did was to kill a cave-bear and take the trophies.

A stone borer, used in making a necklace. When Fleetfoot started out again, he wore a necklace of bear's teeth. He wore them partly because they were trophies and partly because they were charms.

Fleetfoot followed the trail along the edge of the forest until he reached a ridge of hills. Behind him lay the River of Stones and all the places he had known. Before him lay a pretty valley about a day's journey across. To his left the snow-covered mountain peaks shone with a dazzling light.

He stopped only to sleep and to make offerings to the gods. Fleetfoot was full of courage, and yet he was weak from his fast. He longed to be strong against all foes. He longed to be a great hunter. He longed to strengthen his people and to meet the dangers which threatened his clan.

At midday he reached the river, where he sat down to rest. Then he went up the little river, which flowed over a rocky bed.

Fleetfoot followed the river until he came to a spot where it seemed to end. Great masses of snow and ice covered the river bed. Farther up they reached the top of the cliffs and stretched out into the valley.

It was the melting of this glacier which fed the little stream.

Fleetfoot stood and gazed at the glacier with its rough billows of snow and ice. He looked at the green forests which stretched to its very edge. He looked at the great ice sheets which covered the mountain peaks. He looked at the bare crags which jutted out from the rocks. And he wondered if the Big Bear's cave was in one of these rocks.

" It was the melting of this glacier which fed the little stream."

Then he crossed the stream and approached the cliff on the opposite side. There he found a cave, and he looked about, but he found no one at home.

As Fleetfoot was looking about, he began to think of Chew-chew. Everything upon which his eyes rested seemed to speak of her. And yet he could not remember seeing the place before.

Night came again and Fleetfoot slept. Again he saw the Big Bear in his dreams. Again he saw the enemies of his clan, and again he dreamed of his old home.

For several days Fleetfoot explored the country near the mountains. He found several good hunting grounds, but he did not find the Big Bear.

As the days passed it seemed to Fleetfoot that he was no longer alone. He heard no steps, and he saw no tracks; yet he felt sure that some one was near.

One morning, when he awoke, there was some one watching him through the thick leaves. He grasped his spear and was ready to throw, when he heard a merry laugh.

Then a lovely maiden appeared with dark and glossy hair. Her eyes shone with the morning light and her breath was as fresh as the dew.

Fleetfoot dropped his spear and stepped forward to greet the girl. A moment they gazed in each other's eyes, and then they knew no fear.

They sat on a mossy bank where they talked for a long, long time. And Fleetfoot learned that she was called Willow-grouse and that her people were away.

Before he could ask her more, she inquired from whence he came. And then she asked him what had brought him so far away from his home.

While Fleetfoot was telling his story, Willow-grouse listened with sparkling eyes. When he had finished, her eyes fell, and she seemed to be buried in thought. Willow-grouse knew that her own people were plotting against the Bison clan. She wanted Fleetfoot to stay with her; and she feared that if she told him what her people were doing, he would go away.

For a few minutes Willow-grouse kept silent; but, at length, she decided to speak. She told Fleetfoot of the famine of the springtime and of the scarcity of game. She told how the people separated and traveled far and wide. Many of her own people had been to the grounds of the Bison clan. Now the clans were at the rapids. But as soon as the salmon season was over, they were going to attack the Bison clan.

When Fleetfoot heard what Willow-grouse said, he gave up his search for the Big Bear. He decided to go to the salmon feast and learn what the clans were doing. He hoped he could do this and still have time to warn the Bison clan.

THINGS TO DO

See if you can find a way of making a glacier in your sand-box. Model a river valley whose upper part is filled with a glacier. Show where the bed and banks are covered with snow and ice. Show where the cliffs are covered. Show where the ice-sheets are Show on the sand-map Fleetfoot's journey to the place where he fasted. Show the remainder of his journey.

Draw pictures of the following :—
Fleetfoot prays to the fire-god.
Fleetfoot receives signs from the gods.
Fleetfoot standing on the ridge of hills.
Fleetfoot's meeting with Willow-grouse.

XXXII

THINGS TO THINK ABOUT

Can you think why the salmon feast was at the rapids of the river?
Show in your sand-map a place where rapids might be.   If there is
a river near you which has rapids, go to the spot and see if you can
tell what it is that makes the rapids.

Show in your map the hunting grounds of the clans which met at
the rapids.   Find the trails they would follow in going to the rapids.

Find out all you can about the habits of the salmon.

A necklace of fossil shells.

The Meeting of the Clans

At his parting from Willow-grouse, Fleetfoot gave
her a necklace of fossil shells.   Then saying, "We
shall meet when the new moon comes," he started on
his way.

He followed Sweet Brier River on his way to the meeting of the clans. At sunset he knew he was nearing the place where Willow-grouse said they had met. He could hear the roaring of the rapids, and above this sound, the shouts of the clans.

Fleetfoot waited for the cover of darkness, for he did not wish to be seen. Then he approached cautiously toward the spot where the camp fire crackled and blazed. In the light of the flames dark trunks of oaks and fir trees stood out of the blackness. Then moving forms appeared on the banks and lighted the clans seated around the fire. At first Fleetfoot did not go near enough to see the faces distinctly. But he could tell from the various movements that they were preparing for a dance.

All eyes seemed fixed on an old woman who was offering gifts to the gods. She lifted hot stones from the fire and dropped them into a basket of water. Then she took a piece of salmon and dropped it into the water.

As Fleetfoot watched the old woman, he thought of Chew-chew and his old home. Then he wondered if all women would look like Chew-chew when they grew old.

When the offerings were made, the men began a war dance. Some were dressed in masks of horses, and others wore masks of reindeer and cattle.

When the men took off their masks, Fleetfoot looked as if in a dream. For among the strangers moving about there appeared familiar forms.

For a few minutes Fleetfoot could not tell whether he was awake or asleep. What he saw seemed very real, and yet it seemed like a dream. He had almost forgotten his own people. He had not seen them since the day he was lost. And now, only a few paces away, stood Scarface and Straightshaft. Then other familiar forms appeared moving near the fire. And among the women who had beaten the drums were Chew-chew and Eagle-eye.

When Fleetfoot saw his mother and Chew-chew, he almost shouted for joy. He wanted to go and speak to them, but something seemed to hold him back.

Then his heart began to beat so loud and so fast that Fleetfoot was afraid he would be discovered; so he hurried away from the spot to a hollow tree where he spent the nig t.

For a long ti he lay awake thinking about what to do. He c ot go back to Willow-grouse and leave his wo ne. He could not make himself known to Ca who were planning to attack the Bison clan. ld not return to the Bison clan without le e enemies' plans.

And s took the pebble from its bag and asked for aid. Then he fell asleep and di l the break of day.

day he watched the clans. He saw e rapids and feast and play around the e saw them go to a smooth spot near the bank where they played games. When night came he said to himself, "I'll watch the dance and learn their plans."

Scarface offered gifts to the gods before the dance began. As he performed the magic rites, all the people were still. Every eye was turned toward the old man. No one suspected danger.

Fleetfoot, watching from a safe retreat, had heard a rustling sound. And, looking in the direction from which the sound came, he saw a big tiger in a neighboring tree.

The tiger had crept out on a strong branch and was watching for his prey. The eyes of the big cat snapped fire as they followed each movement that Scarface made.

There was not a moment to be lost. The tiger was about to spring. Fleetfoot's spear whizzed through the air and dealt a powerful blow. Another followed, but with less force although Fleetfoot hurled it with all his might.

With a cry of rage the tiger turned, and leaving Scarface upon the ground, he sprang toward Fleetfoot. And the Cave-men grasped their weapons and rushed to the spot.

They found the tiger dying from the effect of the first blow. They watched his death struggles. Then they looked for the man who had hurled a spear that struck a death blow.

If Fleetfoot had not been struck senseless, he might have made his escape. But as it happened, the Cave-men found him lying on the ground, and they raised him up and carried him to a spot near the bright camp-fire.

THINGS TO DO

Show on your sand-map where the clans had camped.   Show where you think Fleetfoot watched.   Show where the ceremonies were performed.

Draw one of these pictures :—

Fleetfoot bids farewell to Willow-grouse.

The clans seated around the camp-fire.

Fleetfoot watching the dance.

Fleetfoot saves Scarface's life.

Watch a cat as it springs upon a mouse, and then think of the tiger as he sprang upon Scarface.   Model it in bas-relief.

XXXIII

THINGS TO THINK ABOUT

What do you think the people will do with Fleetfoot?

Can you think of any way that Fleetfoot might prevent them from attacking the Bison clan?

What Happened when the Clans Found Fleetfoot

While Chew-chew and Eagle-eye were attending to Scarface, others took care of Fleetfoot. They knew nothing about him except that he had saved Scarface's life. Everybody wanted to see him; and so a great crowd gathered around.

People looked at the strange young man as he lay pale and still on the ground. They looked and looked again, then said, "How like he is to Scarface."

Eagle-eye had not forgotten Fleetfoot. She never spoke of him, but she still hoped that he was alive and

that she would see him again.   When strangers came
she always inquired for tidings of the lost boy.

And so when Eagle-eye heard what the people said,
she pushed her way through the crowd.   The moment
she saw him, she cried, "Fleetfoot!" and then bent over
his lifeless form.

Chew-chew, hearing Eagle-eye's cry, hurried to the
spot.   She knelt by his side and murmured his name,
and thought of Scarface when he was young.

Those who stood near turned and asked, "Who is
Fleetfoot?"   Many of the people had never heard of
him.   Others had heard of Eagle-eye's boy.   All were
curious to know more about the strange young man.
All were anxious to know if he was dead or alive.

Fleetfoot was not dead.   He was only stunned by
the tiger's blow   When Eagle-eye bathed him with
cold water, he began to show signs of life.   When at
length he opened his eyes, he knew that he was recognized.

When those who stood near found out who the
young man was, they shouted the tidings to those who
were farther away.   Then the people rejoiced and
thanked the gods for thus befriending them.

Before Fleetfoot slept that night, he wondered how
the meeting would end.   He wondered if he could find
a way to prevent an attack upon the Bison clan.   And,
turning once more to the Big Bear, he soon fell asleep.
Next morning the people caught salmon just below the
rapids.   They feasted a while and then played games
in which Fleetfoot took part.

When the games were over, the young men crowded around him. They asked him how he could throw a spear so as to strike a deadly blow. Fleetfoot told all he knew about the use of spears and harpoons, but he scarcely knew himself how he had thrown with such force.

But he took two spearheads in his hand, just as ne had held them when he saw the tiger. He threw one at a mark and the spear went with such force that the young men shouted for joy. Then they all practiced throwing until they could throw in the same way. It was in this way that people learned to hurl weapons

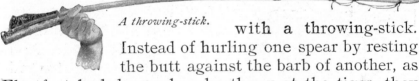

A throwing-stick.

with a throwing-stick. Instead of hurling one spear by resting the butt against the barb of another, as Fleetfoot had done when he threw at the tiger, they learned to shape sticks for throwing spears, and they called them "throwing-sticks."

The older men watched as Fleetfoot showed the young men how he threw spears and harpoons. And soon they all agreed to ask Fleetfoot to lead in the dance that night.

Scarface invited him to lead, and Fleetfoot accepted. He was glad to lead in a real hunting dance, but he was still more glad to have a chance to prevent an attack upon the Bison clan. And so he resolved to plan a dance which would make them forget their plan.

When the time came to begin the dance, Fleetfoot

was ready to lead.   He knew that the men all wanted to find good hunting grounds.   So he showed them where to find such grounds and what trails to follow.

A few days later he went with the people to these very grounds.   There they hunted the bison herds and the Irish deer   And when each of the clans had chosen a place to camp, Fleetfoot bade them farewell.   Then it was that the bravest young men came forward and said that they would follow him.   And so the young men agreed to be brothers and to help one another in times of need.   They agreed upon signs which they should use when they wanted to meet.   And when Fleetfoot started homeward, the young men escorted him.

Of the adventures on the way to the Bison clan's cave there is little time to tell.

An Irish deer.

All the young men where faithful.   And as they journeyed on their way, they recalled Fleetfoot's brave deeds in a victory song.

THINGS TO DO

Show how the people acted from the time Fleetfoot threw his spear until they knew who he was.   Draw pictures which will illustrate the story.

Make such a hunting dance as you think Fleetfoot led. Show in your sand-map the places where the hunting grounds were.

Name all the running games you know. Tell how you play one of them. Draw a picture of the Cave-men playing games.

Make a throwing-stick.

Look at the picture of the Irish deer and tell how it appears to differ from other deer you know. For what do you think it uses its large and heavy antlers?

XXXIV

THINGS TO THINK ABOUT

What do you think Flaker will do while Fleetfoot is gone? What do you think the Bison clan will do when Fleetfoot returns?

Which do you think will be the greater man—Fleetfoot or Flaker?

What things do you think Fleetfoot will do? What do you think Flaker will do?

Fleetfoot's Return

Flaker missed Fleetfoot more than he could tell. Awake, he thought of his dangerous journey. Asleep, he was with him in his dreams. Many, many

A fragment of a Cave-man's baton, engraved with the heads of bison.

times each day he prayed for Fleetfoot's safe return.

Ever since the strangers had camped on their lands, the Bison clan had been anxious. When questioned about it, Greybeard was sad and Bighorn shook his head. So the women were trying to arouse their courage, and Flaker was carving prayers.

When Fleetfoot announced his return, it was Flaker

who heard his whistle.　It was he who shouted the glad tidings to all the Cave-men.　And though he was lame, he was the first who ran ahead to greet him.

Fleetfoot and his companions had halted on a hillside not far from the cave.　It was from this hill that Fleetfoot whistled so as to announce his return. Here his companions waited, while Fleetfoot advanced alone.

While Fleetfoot greeted his friends and showed them his wonderful necklace, his companions chanted his brave deeds in a victory song.　It was thus that the Bison clan learned of Fleetfoot's brave deeds.　It was thus that they learned of his courage which came from fasting and prayer.

When the song was ended, Bighorn advanced with Fleetfoot, and together they escorted the brave young men to the cave of the Bison clan.　There they feasted, and rested, and played games until it was time for Fleetfoot's last test.

Meanwhile the young men became acquainted with Flaker.　Fleetfoot had told them about him.　He had shown them the dagger Flaker made and the engraving of the Big Bear.　And so the young men were glad to see him and make him one of their brotherhood.

When the time came for Fleetfoot's last test, he asked permission to speak.　And when Bighorn nodded his head, Fleetfoot told the people the story of how he and Flaker had worked and played together.　He told of Flaker's bravery the day he was hurt by the bison.　He told of Flaker's poniard which he used to

kill the cave-bear.   He told of the tools which Flaker
had made for working bone and horn.

Then he said that the people of the Bison clan
had taught them to worship the gods.   He said that
Flaker had the favor
of the gods and
that his prayers
would bring success.

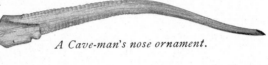

A Cave-man's nose ornament.

And he urged the Cave-men, on account of these
things, to forget that Flaker was lame, and to admit
him into the ranks of the full-grown men.

The Cave-men listened to what Fleetfoot said and
they all gave assent.   And when they made ready to
receive Fleetfoot, Flaker was brought forward.   The
nose of each of the boys was pierced and they were
given nose ornaments.   On account of his bravery
Fleetfoot was given a baton which showed that he
might lead the men.   And Flaker, too, received a baton,
but his was to show that he could lead in the worship
of the gods.

And so every one knew that Fleetfoot and Flaker
were brave young men.   They had passed the tests that
had been given for courage, and patience, and self-
control.   Fleetfoot's companions stayed at the cave
until the ceremonies were ended.   Then they
renewed their vows to help one another and
took leave of the Bison clan.   And Fleetfoot, having done his duty,
was free to return
to Willow-grouse.

*A Cave-man's baton engraved
with wild horses.*

THINGS TO DO

See if you can make such a victory song as you think the young men sang. See if you can make the speech which Fleetfoot made for Flaker
Dramatize this lesson, and then draw a picture of the part you like the best.
See if you can make a baton.

XXXV

THINGS TO THINK ABOUT

Why do you think people began to live in places where there were no caves? Can you think what kind of a shelter they might find?

Find out all you can about the difference between the winter and summer coat of some animal you know.

Which skins do you think would be used for curtains and beds? Which skins would be used for clothing? Which for the heavy winter coats?

Willow-grouse

Soon after the salmon feast, Willow-grouse saw her people again. When they went away, no one knew why she stayed behind. When they returned, no one noticed how eager she was to hear all that was said. So Willow-grouse kept her secret from every one in the clan.

Many days the people hunted; but, at length, there were signs of the coming cold. It was then that the wise men gave an order to prepare for the journey to the winter home.

All but Willow-grouse obeyed; but she heeded not what was said. It was not because she did not hear the command. It was not because she did not care to live with her own people. It was simply because she remembered Fleetfoot and was waiting for his return.

And so, when the women chided her for being a thoughtless girl, they little thought that Willow-grouse was making plans of her own. In the confusion of packing, nobody noticed that she stayed behind, and many moons passed before they learned what Willow-grouse did.

As soon as her people were out of sight Willow-grouse began to make ready for Fleetfoot. There was no cave near at hand, but there were high overhanging rocks. Under one of these the people had camped. They found the roof and back wall of a dwelling ready-made. So they simply camped at the foot of the rock and built their camp-fire.

Willow-grouse knew that the bare rock was a good shelter in summer But she also knew that it would soon be too cold to live in such an open space. So she cut long poles and braced them under the roof so as to make a framework for front and side walls. Then she covered the framework with plaited branches, and left a narrow doorway which she closed with a skin.

It was hard work to make the rock shelter, but Willow-grouse did not mind it. She kept thinking of Fleetfoot all the time, and she hoped the rock shelter would be their new home.

An Eskimo drawing of reindeer caught in snares

When Willow-grouse looked at her dress, she saw it was much the worse for wear. So she set snares in the reindeer trails and caught two beautiful reindeer.

The soft summer skins of the reindeer had short, fine hair. Willow-grouse scraped and pounded them and then polished them with sandstone.

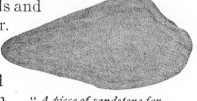

" *A piece of sandstone for flattening seams.*"

Willow-grouse took great pains in making her new garments. She flattened the seams with a piece of sandstone until they were nice and smooth. Then she gathered fossil shells from the rocks and trimmed the neck and sleeves. And she made a beautiful headband and belt, and pretty moccasins for her feet.

And when the time drew near for Fleetfoot's return, Willow-grouse dressed in her new garments. She put on the necklace of fossil shells and thought of Fleetfoot's last words.

Fleetfoot kept his promise. When the new moon came he appeared Then Willow-grouse became his wife and he lived with her in their new home.

A reindeer snare.

THINGS TO DO

Look at the picture of a rock shelter on page 14.

Find some large rocks and put them in your sand-box so as to show a natural rock shelter. Make a framework for front and side walls, and see if you can make it into a warm hut. Model the upper valley. Find a piece of sandstone which you can use in polishing skins.

Dress a doll the way you think Willow-grouse dressed. Dress a doll the way you think Fleetfoot dressed.

Find pretty seeds and shells which you can use in trimming belts and headbands. Before sewing the seeds or shells on the band, lay them so as to make a pretty pattern. After you have made your pattern draw it on paper, so that you can look at it while you are trimming the band.

XXXVI

THINGS TO THINK ABOUT

Look at what you have modeled in your sand-box and see if you can tell in what parts of the valley the snow will be deepest.

When the snow is very deep, what do the wild animals do? What do the people do?

Can you think how people learned to use poison in hunting?

Does the poisoned weapon poison any part of the animal's flesh? Why do people try to be careful not to leave poison around?

How Fleetfoot and Willow-grouse Spent the Winter

When Willow-grouse was living alone, she had to hunt for her own food. Sometimes she caught animals in traps, and sometimes she hunted with spears and harpoons. When the wounded animal escaped, Willow-grouse was disappointed. So she tried all sorts of ways to make sure of the game.

One day she happened to use a harpoon which had been thrust into a piece of decayed liver. She wounded a reindeer with the harpoon and the animal soon died.

And so Willow-grouse soon learned to mix and to use poisons.   When Fleetfoot made simple spearheads

of antler, she helped him make grooves to hold the poison.   When they used poison on their weapons, they were sure of the game without a long chase.

They lived happily in the rock shelter until the middle of winter. Then heavy snowstorms came and the wild animals went away.   Fleet-foot and Willow-grouse were left with-out food.   They ate a piece of sun-dried meat which Willow-grouse had left in a tree; and when that was gone, they put on their snowshoes and started toward the south.

Three views of a Cave-man's spearhead with a groove to hold poison.

Before many days had passed, they arrived at the cave of the Bison clan.   There they were made so wel-come that they stayed for two moons.

It was during this time that the Bison clan learned to use the throwing-stick.   While Fleetfoot taught the use of the throwing-stick, Flaker made wonderful har-poons.   And as fast as Fleetfoot found new ways of using weapons in hunting, Flaker invented new weapons for the men to use.

Ever since Fleetfoot had been away, Flaker had been working at harpoons.   He had made harpoon heads with two or three barbs, and now he was trying to make a harpoon with four or five barbs on each side.

It took a long while to make a harpoon with many beautiful barbs.   It took more patience to make it than most of the Cave-men had. For when Flaker traced a regular outline of the harpoon on one side of the antler, he traced the same outline upon the other side. Then he cut upon these lines, and he shaped the barbs one by one, until he had made them all of the same shape and size.

He finished the base of the head with a large ridge near the end so as to make it easy to attach it to the shaft. Then he traced Fleetfoot's property-mark upon it, and thought that it was done.

But Willow-grouse, who had been watching him, spoke up and said, "No, there is one thing more. You must put a groove in each of the barbs to carry the magic poison."

And so, although Willow-grouse learned a great deal from watching Flaker use his tools, she taught him something he did not know.

When the harpoon was really finished, Flaker gave it to Fleetfoot. And all the Cave-men gathered around to see the new harpoon.

" It was during this time that the Bison clan learned to use the throwing-stick."

When everybody had seen it, Fleetfoot placed the harpoon upon his throwing-stick and hurled it again and again. To the people who stood near, the barbs carried the harpoon through the air like the wings of a bird. The deep grooves which held the poison carried sure death with each wound. And the throwing-stick with which it was hurled helped in getting a firm hold and a sure aim.

Harpoons with several barbs.

THINGS TO DO

Find a piece of soft wood and trace the outline of a harpoon upon it. See if you can whittle a harpoon with barbs.

Experiment until you can tell whether you like to have a ridge on the base of the harpoon head.

Draw one of these pictures :—

"Heavy snowstorms came and the wild animals went away."

Fleetfoot and Willow-grouse find some dried meat in a tree.

Fleetfoot and Willow-grouse arrive at the cave of the Bison clan.

Flaker working at the barbed harpoon.

" The barbs carried the harpoon through the air like the wings of a bird."

XXXVII

THINGS TO THINK ABOUT

How did people sew before they had needles? What bones do you think the Cave-men would use first in making needles and awls? Why would people want the hardest bones for needles?

See if you can find out where the hardest bones are found.

See if you can think of all the things that would have to be done in making a needle out of a piece of ivory or a large bone.

Why do we sometimes wax thread? What do you think the Cave-men would use instead of wax?

Why did the Cave men make holes in their awls? What were the first holes which they made in their needles used for?

How do you think they would think of carrying the thread through the needle's eye?

Why do we use thimbles when we sew? When do you think people began to use thimbles? What do you think the first thimbles were like?

How Willow-grouse Learned to Make Needles

A bone pin.   *A large bone needle.*

Willow-grouse soon made friends with the women. They admired the clothing she wore, and they wanted to learn how to polish skins and to make beautiful clothing. So Willow-grouse showed the women how to polish skins and to make them into beautiful garments.

While the women sewed with bone awls, Willow-grouse watched Flaker, who was sawing a bone with a flint saw.

A bone awl.

It was soon after this that Willow-grouse learned to make needles of large hard bones. The first ones she made were not very beautiful needles. They were not so smooth nor so round as the awls she had made of bird's bones. But she made a beginning and after a while all the women learned to make fine needles.

A bone from which the Cave-men have sawed out slender rods for needles.

A piece of sandstone used by the Cave-men in making needles.

They made the needles of a hard bone which they took from the leg of a horse. They traced out the lines they wished to cut just as Flaker traced the harpoon. Then they sawed out slender rods and whittled one end to a point. The other end they made thin and flat, for this was the end where the hole was made.

They made the rods round and smooth by drawing them back and forth on a piece of soft sandstone. This made long grooves in the sand-stone, which became deeper and deeper every time the sandstone was used. Then they polished the rods by drawing them back and forth between the teeth of a flint comb.

A flint comb used in rounding and polishing needles.

The first needles had no eyes. They were more like awls and pins, than needles. Perhaps the first eyes were made in needles to keep them from getting lost.

It was hard work to saw the bone rods and to round and polish them. No wonder the women did not want to lose

A flint saw used in making needles of bone taken from the leg of a horse.

them. No wonder they bored little holes in the thin flat end and hung them about their necks

It may have been Willow-grouse who first discovered that the eye of the needle could carry the thread. She may have discovered it when she was playing with a needle she carried on a cord. At any rate, the women soon learned to sew with the thread through the needle's eye. And then they began to make finer needles with very small eyes.

A short needle of bone.

These fine needles were used at first in sewing the softest skins. They were used, too, in sewing trimming on beautiful garments. But when the women sewed the hard skins, instead of a needle they used a bone awl.

A flint comb used in shredding fibers.

At the meeting of the clans in the salmon season, the Cave-men wore their most beautiful garments. And soon the clans began to vie with one another in wearing the most beautiful skins. And the women hunted for the choicest sands to use in polishing their needles. They still gave the first polish with a piece of sandstone or a gritty pebble. But when they gave the last polish the women used a powder of the finest sand.

Instead of beeswax, the women used marrow which they kept in little bags. Instead of a thimble, they used a small piece of leather. And instead of pressing the seams with a hot iron, they made them smooth with a rounded stone.

A long fine needle of bone.

From the tough sinews of the large animals, every Cave-man made his own thread. All the children learned to prepare sinew and to shred the fibers with a jagged flint comb.

THINGS TO DO

Find bones which you can make into needles. See if you can find a piece of flint for a saw.

Find a piece of sandstone with which you can polish your needle.

Make a collection of the different kinds of sand in your neighborhood and tell what they can be used for.

Make a collection of needles and find out how they were made.

XXXVIII

THINGS TO THINK ABOUT

If the animals went away in search of shelter from the storms, do you think the Cave-men would know where they went? What do you think they would say when they noticed that the animals had gone?

How did the Cave-men learn what they knew? Why did they make more mistakes than people do to-day?

Two views of a curved bone tool used by the Cave-men in polishing skins.

What changes did the Cave-men see take place in the buds? in seeds? in eggs?

When they found shells in the hard rocks instead of in the water, what do you suppose they would think?

Have you ever heard any one say " It rained angleworms?"

Have you ever heard any one say that cheese or meat had "changed to maggots?"

Can you tell what really happened in each of these cases?

Can you see how stories of animals that turned into men could be started? Is there anything that we can learn from these stories?

How Flaker Became a Priest and a Medicine Man

The winter was long and stormy. Wild animals found little food. Herds of horses and reindeer went to the lowland forests. Game was scarce on the wooded hills. Few horses or reindeer were seen near the caves. The trails were filled with snow and everything seemed to tell of the coming of a famine.

The people ate the frozen meat that was left near the caves, and when they found they could get no more they began to pray to their gods. "O, Big Bear," they prayed, "send us thine aid. Help us now or we die. Drive the horses and reindeer out of thy caverns. Send them back to our hunting grounds."

When the first rumor of famine came, Fleetfoot took down his drum. And he set out over the hills to call a meeting of the brotherhood.

At the first sound of the drumbeat, the people knew what it meant. Everybody felt a gleam of hope. The young men passed the signal along and fresh courage came to the hearts of the people in the neighboring clans.

Buckling their hunger-straps around them, the young men started at Fleetfoot's call. They met near the Bison clan's cave. There they told of the heavy snowstorms and the disappearance of the herds. They told of the beginnings of famine and considered ways of finding food.

11

Some said, "Let us leave the old hunting grounds for our elders.   Let us take wives and go to far away lands."

Others said, "No, let us dwell together and let each clan keep its own hunting ground."

"But how can we dwell together," said one, "when there is not food enough for all?"

The silence which followed the young man's question showed that no one could reply.   It was then that Fleetfoot turned to Flaker and asked him to speak what was in his mind.   And Flaker arose, and turning his eyes toward the heavens, he raised his baton, whereupon all the young men were silent. Then he turned to the young men and said, "The gods will surely provide food for the hungry Cave-men."

A Cave-man's engraving of two herds of wild horses.

"But the people need food and game is scarce," said one of the brave young men. "How can we prevent the famine?   How can we make the gods understand?"

"Remember the Big Bear," said Flaker.   "He heard our prayer when we made his likeness on stone.   Let us make likenesses of the animals.   The gods will then understand our prayers and send many herds to our hunting grounds."

Saying this, Flaker picked up a flint point and a flat piece of stone and quickly engraved two herds of wild horses.   The young men believed in the power of magic.   And when they saw Flaker engraving the herds, they believed the wild horses would come. And so they all tried to make the likeness of an animal they wished to hunt.

When they had made offerings to the gods, the young men were ready to go out to hunt. Flaker stayed at the cave, but it was he who directed them in the right way. He remembered all that the Cave-men had said about the reindeer and the wild horses. And so when they started Flaker said, "Follow the trail to the dense forests."

A Cave-man's carving of horses' heads.

It so happened that just as the young men were starting to hunt, the herds were coming back from the forests. And so the young men had great success, and soon all the Cave-men had plenty of food.

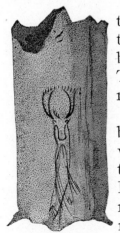

When the young men returned to their homes, they had strange stories to tell. They said that Flaker had brought back the herds by his wonderful magic. They showed the engravings they had made and told of their magical power.

And so wherever stories of Fleetfoot's bravery went, stories of Flaker's magic were told. And just as Fleetfoot worked to learn all the arts of the hunter, so Flaker worked to learn the arts which made him both a priest and a medicine man.

A Cave-man's engraving of a reindeer.

Flaker listened to all the stories that were told by the best hunters. He questioned them eagerly and learned many things which the hunters themselves soon forgot. He learned the haunts of the wild animals in the various seasons. He knew where to look for the best feeding grounds and the places of shelter from storms.

And so when the fame of Flaker was noised about among all the clans, people came from near and from far to make gifts and to get his advice.

THINGS TO DO

Find soft wood or stone and see if you can engrave some animal on it.

Find a stick with branches and carve the head of some animal upon the end of the short branches.

Dramatize this story.

Draw one of these pictures :—

Fleetfoot starting out with his drum.

Flaker speaking to the young men of the brotherhood.

Flaker inquiring of returning hunters about the game and the feeding grounds.

Strangers coming with gifts to get Flaker's advice.

XXXIX

THINGS TO THINK ABOUT

Think of as many simple ways of catching fish as you can. How do you think the Cave-men fished?

What do you think people mean when they say that some one is living a "hand-to-mouth" life?

How do you think people learned to dry meat, fish, or fruit?

Why would the people honor the one who taught them to preserve food by drying it?

Can you think of anything which could be used as food when it was boiled, that would not be a good food eaten raw?

Name a bitter vegetable. What happens to the water in which a bitter vegetable is boiled?

Name a sweet vegetable. What happens to the water in which a sweet vegetable is boiled?

What do you mean by " parboiling ?"

Do you think the Cave-men will learn how to boil food?

How the Cave-men Learned to Boil and to Dry Foods

Again the salmon feast came, and again the neighboring clans camped at the rapids. This time they caught more salmon than they had ever caught before. And this was the summer that the Cave-men began to dry salmon and to fish with harpoons.

It was Willow-grouse who thought of drying salmon, and carrying it to the caves. She remembered the berries dried on the bushes, and the dried meat she found in a tree. No doubt all the Cave-men had eaten dried meat many times before. Often the Cave-men left strips of meat hanging from the trees.

Anybody could leave meat which he did not care to eat. Anybody could eat meat which had been dried in the sun. But not every one was bright enough to think of drying meat.

Chew-chew had never dried meat, nor had any of the women. It was enough for them to prepare the meat which they needed day by day. Few of the people ever thought of laying up stores for the morrow. They lived a "hand-to-mouth" life.

But Willow-grouse remembered the famines. She

knew food was scarce in the early spring. And when she saw the river full of salmon, she thought of the sun-dried meat.

And so Willow-grouse caught some salmon and cleaned them and hung them on the branches of a tree. And when they had dried, she took them down and the Cave-men said that dried salmon were good. And so all the people caught salmon and dried them in the sun.

The first few days the people fished as they had fished before. They waded in the water and caught salmon with their hands, or they stunned them with clubs or with stones. But soon the men began to catch salmon by spearing them with barbed harpoons.

Afterward the Cave-men fished with harpoons which had barbs on only one side. Perhaps they first used a broken harpoon. Perhaps they found they could throw with a surer aim when the barbs were on only one side. At any rate, the Cave-men used harpoons with barbs on one side for fishing, while they used harpoons with barbs on both sides when they went out to hunt.

It was about the time of the salmon feast that people began to boil food. Pigeon first boiled food to eat. She remembered the broth and partly boiled meat which Chew-chew said the gods had left. And she boiled meat and gave it to the men, and they all sounded her praises.

Harpoons of reindeer antler used for fishing.

For a while the only boiling pot Pigeon

used was a hole in the ground which she lined with a skin. Then she used a water-tight basket for boiling little things.

Pigeon always boiled by dropping hot stones into the water. She had never heard of a boiling-pot which could be hung over the fire. She had never heard of a stove. The Cave-men knew nothing about such things as stoves. It would have done them no good if they had, for their boiling-pots could not stand the heat. So instead of putting the boiling-pot over the fire, the Cave-men brought the fire to the boiling-pot by means of hot stones.

In times of famine, Pigeon learned to boil all sorts of roots and leaves. Many bitter plants, when boiled, were changed so that they tasted very well. Some plants which were poison when eaten raw were changed to good foods by being boiled.

A flint harpoon with one barb.

And so the young women had their share in procuring food for the clans. While the young men invented new weapons for hunting, and tried to control the animals by magic, the young women learned to preserve foods and to keep them for times when game was scarce.

When the end of the salmon feast came, the people had dried many salmon. It was soon after this that the young men captured wives and took them to new hunting grounds. And one of the very bravest young men was the one who captured Pigeon.

A spoon-shaped stone made and used by the Cave-men.

THINGS TO DO

Find some kind of raw food which you can dry. Dry it and tell what happens. What dried foods do we eat? In what kind of a place do we keep dried foods?

Find the best way of boiling bitter vegetables. Tell what happens when you boil them. Find the best way of boiling sweet vegetables.

Draw one of these pictures:—

 Catching salmon just below the rapids.

 Drying salmon.

 Pigeon boiling meat for the Cave-men.

XL

THINGS TO THINK ABOUT

Do you think that any of the young men and their wives would live with Fleetfoot and Willow-grouse? Where do you think Flaker will live?

Can you think why Willow-grouse would take great pains to embroider her baby's clothing?

Why would Willow-grouse want pretty colors? Think of new ways she might find of getting pretty colors. How could she get the color out of plants into the stuff she wished to color?

Why was it easier to make pretty dyes after people knew how to boil?

The New Home

A year or so passed and Fleetfoot and Willow-grouse were settled with their kinsfolk in a new rock shelter. Its framework was covered with heavy skins instead of woven branches. Heavy bone pegs and strong thongs served to keep the skins in place.

Flaker and other young men with their wives lived in the rock shelter. There were little children, too, and tiny babies.

A baby's hood.

Willow-grouse had a baby and she thought he was a wonderful child. She dressed him in the softest skins which she embroidered with a prayer. And she hung a bear's tooth about his neck because she thought it was a charm. In winter she put him in a skin cradle and wrapped him in the warmest furs. In summer he played in a basket cradle which Willow-grouse wove on a forked stick.

In all that Willow-grouse did, she always asked the gods for help. The baskets she made for boiling food, were also prayers to the gods.

She searched for the choicest grasses and spread them on a clean spot to dry. No one knew so well as Willow-grouse when to gather the twigs. She knew the season when they were full-grown and gathered them before the sap had hardened. She gathered them when the barks peeled easily and when the rich juices flowed.

When the twigs were gathered the women soaked them and peeled off the bark. They left some of the twigs round, but others they made into flat splints.

" In summer he played in the basket cradle which Willow-grouse wove on a forked stick."

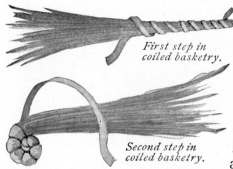

First step in coiled basketry.

Second step in coiled basketry.

Sometimes they stained them with the green rind of nuts, and sometimes they dyed them with pretty dyes.

Instead of weaving the baskets, Willow-grouse sewed them with an over-and-over stitch. In this way she made the soft grasses into a firm basket. She began by taking a wisp of grass in the left hand and a flat splint in the other. She wound the splint around the wisp a few times then turned the wrapped portion upon itself. When she had fastened it with a firm stitch, again she wound the splint around the wisp and took another stitch.

Sometimes Willow-grouse made baskets for boiling food, and sometimes she made them for carrying water. The baskets she prized most were the ones into which she put a prayer. The prayer was a little pattern which she made for a picture of one of the gods. Sometimes it was a wild animal and sometimes it was a bird. Sometimes it was the flowing river and sometimes a mountain peak. And sometimes it was a flash of lightning, and sometimes it was the sun.

Three rows of coiled work.

All the Cave-men wanted the gods to be friendly and they wanted them to stay near.

"*Greybeard, now old and feeble, walked
all the way to the spot.*"

That is why they took so much pains in making pictures of them.   That is why that soon after the rock shelter was made they engraved a reindeer upon the wall.

Greybeard, now old and feeble, walked all the way to the spot.   Fleetfoot and Flaker wanted him to perform the magic rites.

Not all the people who lived there were allowed to take part in the ceremonies.   Only the grown people were allowed to see the first part.   And only the wisest and bravest ones went into the dark shelter.

For a moment, those who went in stood in silence waiting for a sign.   Then, by the light of a torch, Fleetfoot chiseled a reindeer on the hard rock, and Greybeard, holding a reindeer skull, murmured earnest prayers.

A feeling of awe came over them while they worked. They began to feel that the god of the reindeer was really there with them.   They asked the god to take good care of those who lived in the rock shelter, and to send many herds of reindeer to the Cave-men's hunting grounds.

A water basket.

THINGS TO DO

Make a rock shelter with walls of skin instead of plaited branches. Use bone pegs to keep the curtains drawn tight.

Find a forked stick and several smaller ones and make a framework for a basket-cradle. If you cannot weave such a cradle as the one shown in the picture, make one in some other way and fasten it to the frame-work.

Find grasses and splints and see if you can make a sewed mat or basket. Make a simple pattern for your mat.

Look at the picture of a water basket. Why do you think it was made to bulge near the bottom? Why was the bottom made flat? Why was the neck made narrow? Why were handles put on this basket? Tell or write a story about this basket.

Turn to the frontispiece and find a picture with this legend: "A feeling of awe came over them while they worked."

XLI

THINGS TO THINK ABOUT

What might happen that would lead the Cave-men to work together? At what times might the clans help one another?

Think of as many ways as you can of making tents out of poles and skins.

How the Clans United to Hunt the Bison

In spite of all the Cave-men did to appease the wrath of the gods, it seemed to them that a powerful god was trying to do them harm. Soon after the bison came, the grass near the caves disappeared. Then the herds scattered and the Cave-men said, "The god has driven them away."

As the word passed from cave to cave, all the people were frightened. Wise men shook their heads and looked about in despair. Then it was that the younger men spoke of Fleetfoot and Flaker.

Scarface knew of Fleetfoot's courage. And when he heard of Flaker's magical power, he sent messengers, bearing gifts, to invite them with their people to a meeting of the clans.

Fleetfoot and Flaker accepted the gifts and made ready to go. The women made a stretcher for Flaker. And when they had buried their household treasures, all set out to the meeting of the clans.

They arrived at the Fork of the River where Fleetfoot had lived when he was a child. There the frightened clans had gathered to seek aid against a common foe.

When the people saw Flaker upon the stretcher, their voices were hushed and all was still. And when Flaker, arising, fixed his eyes upon something that no one else could see, they scarcely breathed. They were sure that something was going to happen.

Instead of offering gifts, Flaker threatened the angry god. He made faces at him; he shook his fists, and he made a great noise. And the people, becoming excited, joined Flaker in making threats. They made faces, they joined hands, they danced about and they made such a horrible noise that they began to feel that the god was frightened and that he had gone away.

When the ceremony was ended, the people hoped to find the herds. Scarface asked for young men to go ahead and act as scouts. Several young men at once stepped forward from different parts of the circle of the clans. And Scarface selected Fleetfoot and Blackcloud to go in search of the herds.

The people listened as Scarface spoke thus to the young men: "Go follow the tracks, listen to each sound; find where the herds are feeding. Do not frighten them away. Return quickly and report what you have seen. If you speak not the truth when you

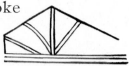

A Cave-man's engraving of a tent showing the interior structure.

return, may the fire burn you; may the lightning strike you; may the Big Bear shut you in his dark cavern!"

The scouts nodded their heads, and looked to Flaker for a sign. And Flaker, turning to the scouts, said, "The gods will lead you. Follow where the green grass is cropped. Follow where the grass is trampled. These are the signs which the gods will give to show that you are on the right way."

A Cave-man's engraving of a tent showing the exterior.

The scouts departed. The first day the clans made ready to move. The second day the scouts returned and brought news of the herds. The third day all the clans were traveling toward the fertile plains.

Fleetfoot and Blackcloud led the way and at midday caught sight of the herds. At once, Fleetfoot gave the signal and Scarface ordered the clans to stop. Then the men prepared to attack the herds, while the women built the tents.

There were no large trees in sight, but there were a few small ones. A grassy plain stretched all

A Cave-man's engraving of a tent with covering pulled one side so as to show the ends of the poles which support the roof.

around for a long, long way. And so the women built their tents out of slender saplings.

Most of the women made a framework by leaning poles against the branch of a tree. The roof and the walls of such a tent were one and the same thing. Willow-

Framework showing the best kind of a tent made by the Cave-men.

grouse and her companions tried a different way.

It was by trying different ways in the different places where they camped, that the women at length learned to make tents with the roof separated from the wall. The Cave-men made pictures of some of these tents upon a piece of antler.

When the men parted from the women, they considered ways of attacking the herd. It was hard to approach it on the grassy plain without being seen. And the men knew that if the herd was alarmed, it would gallop far away.

At length Fleetfoot showed the Cave-men a plan for surrounding the herd. And he asked who would volunteer to follow two leaders in separate lines.

All the bravest men volunteered, for they were eager to make an attack. Fleetfoot placed them in two lines and told them what each one was to do.

Fleetfoot led one of the lines through the

A tent pin

grass to the right, and Blackcloud led the other to the left. They crept softly through the tall grass until they had surrounded the herd. Approaching the herd cautiously, they drew nearer and nearer together.

Fleetfoot gave the signal to attack when they were about a spear's throw away   At once the harpoons whizzed through the air and struck many a mortal blow. The bison were taken by surprise and they attempted to escape. But no sooner had they run from one side than they were attacked from the other.

Many a bison was killed that day and many others were wounded. Many of the Cave-men carried away marks of an ugly bison's horns.

But all of the people had food and all the people were happy. And to show that they honored both Fleetfoot and Flaker they bored holes through their batons.

THINGS TO DO

Make such a stretcher as you think the women made to carry Flaker.
Make tents whose roof and walls are one and the same thing. Make a tent whose roof and walls are separated. Tell how you think people learned to make such perfect tents.
Dramatize one of the following scenes and then draw a picture to illustrate it :—

The fear of the people at the disappearance of the herds
Bearing gifts to Fleetfoot and Flaker.
Flaker threatening the angry god.
Sending the scouts.
Surrounding the herds.
Showing honors to Fleetfoot and Flaker

XLII

THINGS TO THINK ABOUT

If there were not men enough to surround a herd can you think of anything the Cave-men might do to drive them where they wanted them to go?

How do we get animals into traps?

Why do you think people first began to make fences and walls?

How do you think they used them?

Why do we have fences? What do we use them for?

How Things were Made to Do the Work of Men

When the clans returned to their own hunting grounds, they could not surround the large herds. There were not enough men in one cave to hunt in this way Sometimes they partly surrounded a herd and drove the animals over a cliff, but unless the herd was near the cliff, there were not enough men to drive them.

And so the men tried to coax the animals to the edge of the cliff. Sometimes they did it by imitating the cries the animals made. Sometimes they did it by dressing so as to look like the animals themselves. But even then they often failed to get the animals into their trap.

It was when Fleetfoot saw a bison frightened by a feather that he thought of making things do the work of live men.

The greater part of the day the bison fed some dis-tance from the cliff. Fleetfoot wanted to find a way of driving them up to the very edge.   The bison drive which he invented was the way he succeeded in doing it.

It was shaped like a letter V with the point cut off The sides were piles of brush, or stones, or vines stretched from tree to tree.   At the edge of the cliff where they started, the sides were only a short distance apart.   But the farther out they extended, the farther they were apart.

Men, women, and children joined in making the bison drive.   They piled stones and heaped up brush, and they hunted for long vines.   Then they hunted for feathers and bits of fur, which they tied along the lines.

Flaker performed the magical ceremony before the hunt began.   Fleetfoot dressed in a bison's skin so as to coax the herd along   Women and children hid behind piles of stone and brush.   And the men formed themselves in line far out from the cliffs in the rear of the herd.

Everybody kept still until Fleetfoot's signal sounded. Then the men sprang up and with loud shouts they ran after the herd.   The bison saw Fleetfoot in disguise; and, thinking he was one of the herd, they followed where he led.

When the bison came near a pile of stones a woman or child frightened them.   When they came near the fence of vines they were frightened away by the feathers and fur   And so the herd kept on toward the steep cliff

And with loud shouts and drumbeats, with the clatter of weapons and hard hoofs, the bellowing herd galloped madly on toward the steep cliff. Then Fleet-foot, throwing off his disguise, slipped under one of the lines; but the frantic herd rushed headlong to the brink of the precipice. Then, seeing the danger, the fore-most ones attempted to escape. But the maddened herd pressed blindly on and pushed them over the cliff.

After such a hunt as this, there was food enough for many days. Very likely the women dried meat during this time.

THINGS TO DO

Model in your **sand-box** *a good place for the bison drive. Make the drive and show what happened from first to last.*

Draw one of these pictures :—

 Bison feeding some distance from the cliff.

 Building a bison drive.

 Fleetfoot leading the herd.

 The bison at the edge of the cliff.

 Drying meat.

XLIII

THINGS TO THINK ABOUT

Can you think why people make rules and laws? Why do we have them?

What kind of rules and laws do you think the Cave-men made?

What laws do you think they would make about hunting animals?

What laws would they make about the use of plants?

What people did the Cave-men honor most? What must any one do to be honored? What were some of the signs that a man was honored?

When dangerous work needs to be done, what kind of men and women are needed?

After the bison hunt.

How the Cave-men Rewarded and Punished the Clansmen

Again the clans went to hunt on the fertile plains. Again the women built the tents while the men went out to hunt.   But before the tents were finished, the women heard the thunder of the galloping herd. Angry shouts followed, and the women began to feel alarmed.

All the men were angry with Blackcloud. He had frightened the herd away.   Fleetfoot had planned to surround the bison as they were surrounded before. But a stronger and braver young man than Blackcloud, helped Fleetfoot lead the lines. Nobody dreamed that Blackcloud would do it. Everybody knew that each one must be careful not to frighten the herd.   The men crept quietly through the grass when they saw a bison browsing near the line.   But when Blackcloud saw a young cow, he rushed forward and made an attack.

Handle of a Cave-man's hunting-knife with engraving of a man hunting the bison.

The loud bellow of the wounded cow gave the alarm to the herd. And before the Cave-men could stop them, the bison were galloping madly away.

And so all the men were angry with Blackcloud. Bighorn wanted to have him flogged.   Others wanted to kill him.   He dared not come near them for many days.   No one would hunt with him, and no one would give him food.

Afterward, when he begged to be taken back, the people let him come.   But first they gave him a hard flogging in the presence of the clan.

As years passed, the custom grew of making rules for the hunt.   And those who broke any of the rules were punished by the clan.

Every day the Cave-men recited the brave deeds of the clan.   They watched every one carefully, so as to know who the brave men were.   Those who were found most useful

A hunter's tally

to the clan were given special honors.   And when a man did a very brave deed he was given a hole in his baton.

Brave hunters, besides keeping trophies, engraved a record of their brave deeds.   Sometimes they kept a hunter's tally, and sometimes they engraved the animal they killed.

Many of the Cave-men engraved these records upon the weapons they used in the chase.   They believed that the weapons which had such engravings were of great value for their magical powers.   The wise men, who led the people, engraved their records upon their batons.

Fragment of Cave-man's baton engraved with reindeer.

Others engraved them upon their trophies or upon bone hairpins which they used in their hair.

The engraving of a seal upon a bear's tooth probably recorded a trip to the sea, while the rude sketch of the mammoth made on the mammoth's tusk, probably recorded a great hunt.

Engraving of a seal upon a bear's tooth.

By all these signs of brave deeds, the Cave-men knew who the brave men were. And these same records help to tell the story of THE LATER CAVE-MEN.

THINGS TO DO

Write out some of the rules you have helped make for your games. Do you think the rules are good ones?

See if you can engrave or carve an ornament on some weapon you have made. Before doing it, think what you would like to have the ornament mean.

Draw one of these pictures:—

"All the Cave-men were angry with Blackcloud."

Engraving records upon trophies and batons.

Tell a story of how bone hairpins came to be used.

Tell a story of the Cave-men's trip to the sea.

Tell a story of a mammoth hunt.

A Cave-man's hairpin engraved with wild horses.

SUGGESTIONS TO TEACHERS

H.V.B.

"THE Industrial and Social History Series," of which this is the third number, emphasizes, first of all, the steps in the development of industrial and social life. But in addition to its use as a series of text-books in history or social science, it has a place as a mode of approach to the different subjects included in the curriculum of the elementary school. Whether the work suggested under "Things to Think About" and "Things to Do" is carried out in the period devoted to the study and recitation known as history (possibly some may prefer to call it reading), or in those periods devoted to geography, nature study, language, constructive work, and art, is largely a question of administration. The point for the teacher to make sure of is that the interests of the child which are aroused through the use of the books be utilized not merely in history, but in geography, nature study, reading, language, constructive work, and art. If this is done, subjects which too long have been isolated from the interests of real life, will become the means of stimulating and enriching all of the activities of the child.

The list of references and the tabulated facts presented in *The Early Cave-men*, pp. 159–165, will be of service to the teacher who wishes to engage in a further study of the subject.

SPECIAL SUGGESTIONS

Lesson I. It seems best to let the child read the first story before asking questions. Afterwards, however, the following questions may be of service: Did you ever see a reindeer? Where do reindeer live now? Where were the reindeer at the time of the Tree-dwellers? Where were they at the time of the early Cave-men? (See *The Tree-dwellers*, pp. 125–129, and *The Early Cave-men*, pp. 163–167.) Why did the reindeer come to the wooded hills by the caves at the time of the Cave-men? Why do reindeer live in herds? Name other animals that live in herds. Do you think the reindeer herds would stay near the caves all the year?

Should any child inquire how we know that it was once very cold here, tell him of the tracks that the glaciers made, and of the work of the glaciers in grinding hard rocks so as to make fertile soil. Let the children turn to the picture of a glacier on page 136, and let them hunt for a rock which has markings made by glacial action. But reserve the fine points of this topic for a later period.

The children will be helped to get a conception of the great number of reindeer in a herd partly through the story, partly through illustrations, and partly through tearing reindeer from paper and mounting them so as to represent great herds. The child's experiences in seeing processions or large numbers of people assembled can also be used in forming a picture of the large number of reindeer that met at the ford.

In this and in succeeding lessons, which refer to the women carrying the fresh meat to the cave, remember that animals no larger than the reindeer were carried to the cave. Larger animals, such as the wild horse, the cow, and the bison, were divided on the spot. The bones having the greater amount of flesh were removed from the carcass and carried to the cave where the flesh was eaten and the bones left. Three women could carry the flesh of one bison without the skin. When the skins were good they were carried to the cave. In addition to the skin and the flesh the Cave-men prized the head as a trophy and also as a means of gaining control over the animals by sympathetic magic. All the skulls were broken, probably for the sake of removing the brains, which are usually considered a delicacy among primitive peoples.

Lesson II. Help the children to see that when people had no books, the person who knew most was of great service to the clan. The older people, because they had more experience, took the place of books. That is one reason why people were glad to take care of older and wiser people than themselves, when the latter were no longer able to do hard work.

Lesson III. This lesson illustrates one form which education among primitive peoples takes. Relate what is given regarding the speed of the wild horse in the lessons on pp. 61–71, in *The Tree-dwellers*, which show the influence of such flesh-eating animals as wolves in developing the speed of the wild horse on the grassy uplands.

Lesson IV. This lesson illustrates the ideas of primitive peoples regarding sickness and methods of treating the sick, which consisted largely of ceremonies for driving the "angry god," the "evil spirit," away. In dealing with a superstition of primitive peoples always try to lead the child to discover the mistaken idea which gave rise to it.

Lesson V. Let the children experiment in making straight shafts. The value of this work is not in the product—the shaft—but in its power to arouse the inventive spirit, to call forth free activity, and to yield an experience which lies at the basis of a great variety of subjects.

Reference: Katharine E. Dopp, *The Place of Industries in Elementary Education*, pp. 133, 140, 145.

Lesson VI. In most places throughout the United States there is some one who has a small collection of Indian arrows. If the children can see some of these arrows or other flint implements, it will add greatly to their interest in this subject. In places where flint can be found, the children should collect specimens and experiment in chipping and flaking off small pieces. Where no flint is to be found, it is possible to get good specimens by exchanging materials with children in other localities.

References: Katharine E. Dopp, *The Place of Industries in Elementary Education*, pp. 72, 138–140.

Lessons VII and VIII. The habit horses have of pawing the ground is thought to be a survival of the ancient habit of pawing snow away from the grass. The horses and reindeer stayed in the neighborhood of the caves all through the winter, going to protected places only in times of severe storms. The bison and wild cattle, on the contrary, went to the lowland plains and forests at the close of summer, and returned only after the snow had melted.

Since few children now have the opportunity to observe the bison, and no child has the opportunity to see great herds, they must rely upon books, pictures, and other symbols as sources for the necessary facts. In bringing the sources of knowledge to the children, the teacher should remember that the modern European bison, which is a descendant of the aurochs of Pleistocene times, the species of bison we are considering, is smaller than the ancient form. The Pleistocene bison of Europe was similar to the American type that lived in the woodlands.

Although the teacher should make use of available materials in supplying herself with information regarding the bison, the following summary is presented, especially for those who do not have access to public libraries.

The bison are naturally shy, avoiding the presence of man; they have a keen sense of smell, and hence man has difficulty in approaching a herd, except from the leeward side. They have little intelligence, are sluggish and timid, rarely attacking man or beast, except when wounded or in self-defense. In migrating they travel in large herds, but when feeding they separate into herds of about two or three hundred each. The leader maintains his position by superior intelligence and brute force. If he fails in duty he is punished. Scouts go ahead of the herd in search of new pastures; and guards, or sentinels surround the herd and guard it while feeding and during the night. When the guards have been on duty awhile, they give place to fresh guards. In case of danger, the guards give a signal of alarm by tossing up the head and bellowing furiously. At this the leader gives a signal and the herd starts off at once. Bison run swiftly for a short distance, but are not able to continue a rapid flight. They can run faster than cattle, however, and when pursued always run against the wind. When surprised or wounded, they turn upon their assailants and attack them furiously, fighting with horns and hoofs. They show their rage by thrusting out the tongue, lashing the tail, and projecting the eyes. At such times they are fierce and formidable. The enemies of the bison are the carnivorous animals. A herd of bison has no cause to be afraid of wolves or bears, but solitary bison are often killed by these creatures. The cry of a bison resembles that of a groan or grunt. In case the leader is killed and no bison is able to assert his authority, there is great confusion until the question of leadership is settled.

References: Richard Irving Dodge, *The Plains of the Great West*, pp. 119–147. W. T. Hornaday, *The Extermination of the American Bison*, in "The Smithsonian Report of the U. S. National Museum," 1887, pp. 367–548. Poole's Index will supply references to magazines, and the encyclopedias and natural histories will furnish further facts.

Lessons IX and X. Boiling is such a common process that one seldom thinks of the importance of the discovery of the art. These lessons will show the child how people may have learned to boil and the explanation they would be apt to give of the changes which take place during the process. Boiling was undoubtedly used as a religious ceremony long before it was used for cooking food.

Lessons XI and XII. If possible let the children take a field trip in connection with these lessons. If there are no nuts or wild fruits to gather, let the children gather fruits from a garden or some of the products of the farm. The particular conditions in which the children are placed will determine the form this lesson shall take. At any rate, there will be an opportunity to observe birds, squirrels, or rabbits.

Lessons XIII and XIV. The shelter described is a very early form and is important as a step in the evolution of shelter. The remains found give ample evidence that such a form was adopted by the Cave-men of France.

Lesson XV. It was a common practice among primitive peoples to adopt a child or even a grown person into the clan. The custom is important as revealing one method of introducing new ideas at a time when means of communication were undeveloped.

The description of the method of softening skins by beating and treading upon them illustrates the common use of rhythm and song as a means of holding the attention to what otherwise would be tedious work.

Lessons XVI and XVII. The data for these lessons is taken from drawings made by the Cave-men and from the results of anthropological research among primitive peoples. It will be best not to confine the children to any one mode of clothing, but to allow them to express their own ideas regarding the first forms used.

Lesson XVIII. In connection with this lesson the children will be interested in observing the signs of a storm, the actions of animals before and during a storm, methods they adopt to protect themselves, as well as the animals and birds which migrate from the place where the children live.

Lesson XIX. Let the children think of ways in which snowshoes might be invented, and the things the Cave-men would be able to do after having the snowshoes.

Lesson XX. The invention of traps requires more forethought than the invention of weapons and was at a later date. The accidental catching of animals in natural traps, such as vines, pot-holes, soft places in the marshes and cliffs, offered a suggestion; and the tediousness of lying in wait, on the one hand, and the danger of a direct conflict with large animals, on the other, offered a strong motive for the use of nature's suggestions in the way of traps. Undoubtedly women made a large use of traps in catching the smaller animals before men gave much attention to this mode of hunting.

If the children make as many simple traps as they can think of and arrange them in the order of their complexity, they will be able after a few months to work out a fairly complete series in the evolution of traps.

Lesson XXI. This lesson illustrates the constant interaction between man's inventions and the animal's habits. A new invention which gives man greater power in hunting, makes the animals more timid, more watchful, more skillful in escaping from man's presence. Hence, man is constantly stimulated to make new inventions, in order to be successful in the hunt.

Reference: Katherine E. Dopp. *The Place of Industries in Elementary Education.* (See Index under *Animals* and *Traps.*)

Lesson XXII No animal was more difficult to hunt than the wild horse. Herds of horses were organized under a leader and sentinels which were very alert in detecting the least sign of danger; and as soon as the alarm was given, the herds would run with great speed until they were out of sight When unable to escape they would fight furiously with hoofs and teeth. When in need of a new pasture, scouts—the old, experienced, wise, cautious, and observant members of the herd—

would be sent out to search for good feeding grounds and to report to the herd.

Lesson XXIII. Help the children to see that, although the children of the caves did not go to such schools as we have, they had lessons to learn and tests to take. Those who lived together had to learn to work together. Each one must learn to be patient, brave, and self-controlled. The thoughtless, impatient, and cowardly were apt to prevent the capture of wild animals in the hunt, and to risk the lives of their clansmen. Hence, from early childhood the old men and women gave attention to teaching the children, preparing them for the tests which must be passed before they ranked with the men and women.

Lesson XXIV. Instances of stags meeting death by having their horns interlocked are well known.

Lesson XXV. Encourage the children to notice the difference between those animals which live in herds and those which lead a solitary life. Although the dog has changed greatly since it was domesticated, a study of the dog will be helpful in understanding the habits of packs of wolves. Jack London's *Call of the Wild*, and Ernest Thompson Seton's stories will be helpful in this connection. The cat, having changed less than the dog, will furnish the child with a good type of carniverous animals that lead a solitary life.

Lesson XXVI. From an examination of the skeletons which have been referred to the late Pleistocene period, it is evident that the Cave-men were able to treat wounds and to set bones. "No one could have survived such wounds as we have described," writes Mr. Nadaillac, "but for the care and nursing of those around him, such as the other members of his tribe. The wounded one must have been fed by the others for months; nay more, he must have been carried in migrations, and his food and resting place must have been prepared for him."

Lesson XXVII. There was little difference between weapons and tools until the period of the later Cave-men. A piece of chipped stone served as a tool and a weapon. The children learned when they read *The Tree-dwellers* how people used the tools in their bodies and how they supplemented these by the use of natural tools, such as sticks, stones, shells, bones, and horns. In reading *The Early Cave-men* they learned how people chipped flint and bound strong handles to heavy spear points and axes. At this time they can learn how people came to make use of new materials—materials which require the use of *tools* in shaping into weapons. Tools had been used by women from a very early time. The digging-stick, the hammer-stone, the chopper, the knife, and the bone awl are tools which every woman used. Men, on the contrary, were more interested in weapons than in tools, and it is quite likely that the first steps which led to the differentiation of tools from weapons was made by a man who had been wounded and thus disabled for the hunt.

The incident of Bighorn making fun of the bone dagger is introduced to illustrate the conservative tendency which is still present in society, a tendency less powerful now than in early times, yet strong enough to keep many people out of sympathy with the forces which work for progress.

Let the children examine a real antler, if possible, and notice its fitness for being made into a variety of tools and weapons. If no antler can be found let them examine the picture of one, so as to determine what part of it is used in making a dagger, a hammer, a baton, a tent peg, and an awl.

Lesson XXVIII. The invention of the flint saw marks an important step in the evolution of both tools and weapons. Without the saw it would have been impossible to use such material as bone, horn, and ivory. It is interesting to notice that the saw was at first not clearly differentiated from the file and the knife, the three tools being united in one piece of flint.

Lesson XXIX. In representing the action of a story by means of pantomime, let the children choose a leader who shall take charge of the action. Where this has been tried the results have been very satisfactory. The children, because they feel the responsibility, are stimulated to their best thought. The pleasure they take in the play leads them to a far more careful study of the book than they would make without this stimulus. In addition to this, it leads them to be alert in making use of various sources of knowledge.

Lesson XXX. Hunting peoples, because they live a hand-to-mouth life, have either a feast or a famine. Game was so plentiful during the late Pleistocene period that we may suppose that the Cave-men usually had plenty of food. The time when a famine was most likely to occur was early spring, before the grass furnished food for the herds which came a little later. When food supplies begin to fail, the clan breaks up into smaller groups, and, in case of great scarcity, each of these groups subdivides so that food may be found.

The worship of the bear and other large animals can be traced back to a very ancient period. It undoubtedly originated in the Pleistocene period when man first stood in fear of these animals and tried to win their favor by offering gifts.

Lesson XXXI. In Central France, the region from which the greater part of the data used in this book is derived, small glaciers were to be found in the upper portions of the mountain valleys, but they did not extend far down the river valleys. In other places, however, glaciers extended far down into the lowlands.

While this is not the place for a thorough study of the glacier, it is possible for the children of primary grades to understand certain phases of the subject. The teacher who attempts to make clear the formation of the glacier may find the following quotation from Prof. Shaler helpful: "When a glacial period comes upon a country, the sheets of ice are first imposed upon the mountain tops, and then the ice creeps down the torrent and river beds far below the snow line, in a manner now seen in Switzerland and Norway. As long as the ice streams follow the torrent-channels, they act in something like the fashions of the flowing waters—to gouge out the rocks and deepen the valleys; but as the glacial period advances and the ice sheet spreads beyond the mountains enveloping the plains as well, when the glacier attains the thickness of thousands of feet, it disregards the valleys in its movements and sweeps on in majestic march across the surface of the country. As long as the continental glaciers remain the tendency is to destroy the river valleys. The result is to plane down the land and, to a certain extent, to destroy all preëxisting river valleys."

If this subject is studied while snow is on the ground it will be interesting to the children to experiment out of doors in making glaciers. If there are no hills present the children can readily make small hills on their playground and the falling and partial melting of the snow will do the rest.

Lesson XXXII.   Neighboring clans are accustomed to meet at the rapids of a river during the salmon season.   At such places, and in all places where abundant sources of food are to be found, neighboring clans participate in feasting, dancing, and general merrymaking.   Just as scarcity of food tends to separate people, so abundance of food tends to draw them together.   At such gatherings people of different clans exchange ideas, learn new ways of doing things and become accustomed to act in larger groups for the accomplishment of a common purpose.

Lesson XXXIII.   On the side of invention the throwing-stick is a point to be emphasized in this lesson.   On the side of social coöperation, the organization of the brotherhood is the point of interest.   Such organizations are characteristic of primitive peoples, and similar organizations among children are of common occurrence.

Lesson XXXIV.   This lesson serves to bring out the contrast between Fleetfoot, the brave, active young man, who is beginning to develop the arts which require great personal bravery and force, and Flaker, the crippled young man, whose ability is directed toward the development of tools and the arts which later make him a priest and medicine man.   Originally, there was no sharp distinction between the priest and the medicine man.   One person performed both functions, and in many cases this person was a woman.   Later, those who made use of supplication and entreaty constituted the priesthood, while those who attempted to frighten the gods were known as medicine men.

Lesson XXXV.   Overhanging rocks were made use of for natural shelters from the earliest times.   The improvement of the natural shelter by the addition of front and side walls was a later step and was doubtless an invention of woman.   The motives for such an invention may be found in the fact that in many places near good hunting grounds there were not enough caves to shelter the people.   Under such circumstances, as well as in districts where no caves abound, women would not be slow to take advantage of the overhanging rocks and to use their ingenuity in converting them into comfortable habitations.

Let the children compare summer and winter skins, if possible; if not, let them notice the difference between the horse's coat in winter and summer.

Lesson XXXVI. To help the children to realize the importance of the discovery of the use of poison, let the children think of the many advantages which the Cave-men enjoyed because they could use it.

The dependence of man upon animals for his food supply is shown here. The disappearance of the herds caused Fleetfoot and Willow-grouse to leave the rock-shelter. This is the beginning of a series of events which culminates in a famine. With this in mind, the teacher can emphasize the points which lead up to the famine.

Lesson XXXVII. Let the children bring together from various sources the materials and tools required to make needles by the processes of the Cave-men. Do not require the children to make needles, but permit them to experiment with the materials so as to understand the subject. If the children label and arrange the collection they make in an orderly way, the work itself will be of great value to them, and the collection will constitute an interesting feature in the children's industrial museum.

Lesson XXXVIII. Such a lesson as this ought to be helpful in freeing the child from superstitions without putting him out of sympathy with people who entertain them. In their origin superstitions are unsuccessful attempts to explain the phenomena of life. In spite of the fact that many of the beliefs of mankind have been false, they have served a useful purpose in the development of the individual and in uniting individuals into social groups.

The art of the cave-men, as illustrated in this and in other lessons, shows a belief in sympathetic magic, a belief that is universal among primitive peoples. The fear formerly entertained by the American Indians of having their photographs taken was due to a belief in sympathetic magic. The one who possessed the likeness was supposed to have some mysterious power over the person.

Help the children to distinguish between the things the Cave-men did which really helped and those which they thought helped. Notice that Flaker actually learned a great deal about the topography of the country, the location of the best hunting grounds, the movements and habits of the herds, and, because of this, was often able to give the Cave-men good advice. The magical ceremonies he practiced were of use to him in getting the people to believe in his wonderful power. (See, also, notes under *XXXIV*.)

Lesson XXXIX. Although there was a great variety and abundance of fish, not all the Cave-men used fish. From the remains which have been found, however, we know that different clans used nearly all the varieties of fish which still may be found in our rivers and lakes; and we may readily believe that a salmon stream would be held as property common to all the neighboring tribes, as it is to-day among hunting and fishing peoples.

Fishing tackle of the Cave-men was very crude. Fish were sufficiently abundant, however, to be caught with the hands or by means of stones and clubs. A fish hook made of a bear's tooth, by removing the enamel and crown and lessening the thickness by rubbing, has been found. The barbed harpoons, which were originally made for hunting, were later used in spearing fish. Harpoons with barbs on both sides were well adapted for throwing through the air, while those with barbs on one side were better adapted for use in the water. An experiment with a pencil in a glass of water will show the child that the part in the water is not where it appears to be, and from this he can readily reach the conclusion given above.

Lesson XL. If one will notice the clothing and the cradles of the North American Indians in a museum, he cannot fail to observe that care was taken in their preparation. They are comfortable and, in many cases, beautiful. We may well believe from what is known that among all primitive peoples the beauty, especially that of ornamentation, was for the sake of some supposed magical power. The representation of an animal was supposed to secure the especial protection of that animal, which was worshiped as a god. The bear's tooth, which was pierced and strung about the neck of an infant, served a useful purpose when the child was cutting teeth, and it was supposed to be a charm which served to protect the child.

Lesson XLI. The strongest motives for coöperation were doubtless the common need of protection from dangerous beasts of prey and the need of adopting methods of hunting wild animals which required the united efforts of many people. Notice that the different batons and fragments of batons represented in this book differ in the number of holes bored through them. It is thought that the number of holes indicated the rank of the owner. Although many theories are given regarding the use of batons, the one which seems most tenable to the author is that which views them as marks of distinction and instruments used in magical ceremonies and in hunting dances.

Lesson XLII. The method of hunting herds by surrounding them is a coöperative method suitable to such regions as grassy plains, and comparatively level tracts which are sparsely wooded. The drive, on the contrary, is adapted to regions where steep cliffs are to be found. It is a natural development of the earlier method of hunting by taking advantage of the proximity of animals to steep cliffs. In that case man's part was to lie in wait until a favorable opportunity presented itself for frightening the animals over. The lesson in *The Tree-dwellers* on "How the Hyenas Hunted the Big-nosed Rhinoceros," and the one in *The Early Cave-men* on "Hunting the Mammoth," illustrate early stages of this method.

Notice that there is a new principle employed in this lesson—that of the decoy—and that the method of hunting by means of the drive makes use of various ideas worked out before.

Lesson XLIII. The experience of children in games is sufficient to enable them to realize the necessity of making laws and rules for regulating the conduct of the members of the group. This lesson should serve to connect this narrow experience with that of the race.

Many of the representations of the Cave-man's art, as shown in the illustrations of this book, might well have been made the subjects of special lessons. The limits of this book, however, forbid further expansion.

Industrial and Social History Series

By KATHARINE ELIZABETH DOPP, Ph. D.
Lecturer in Education in the Extension Division of the University of Chicago. Author of
"The Place of Industries in Elementary Education."

WHAT THE BOOKS ARE

Book I. THE TREE-DWELLERS. The Age of Fear.

Illustrated with a map, 15 full-page and 46 text drawings in half-tone by Howard V. Brown. Cloth, square 12mo, 158 pages; 45 cents. For the primary grades.

THIS volume makes clear to the child how people lived before they had fire, how and why they conquered it, and the changes wrought in society by its use. The simple activities of gathering food, of weaving, building, taming fire, making use of stones for tools and weapons, wearing trophies, and securing coöperative action by means of rhythmic dances, are here shown to be the simple forms of processes which still minister to our daily needs.

Book II. THE EARLY CAVE-MEN. The Age of Combat.

Illustrated with a map, 17 full-page and 68 text drawings in half-tone by Howard V. Brown. Cloth, square 12mo, 183 pages; 45 cents. For the primary grades.

IN this volume the child is helped to realize that it is necessary not only to know how to use fire, but to know how to make it. Protection from the cold winters, which characterize the age described, is sought first in caves; but fire is a necessity in defending the caves. The serious condition to which the cave-men are reduced by the loss of fire during a flood is shown to be the motive which prompts them to hold a council; to send men to the fire country; to make improvements in clothing, in devices for carrying, and in tools and weapons; and, finally, to the discovery of how to make fire.

Book III. THE LATER CAVE-MEN. The Age of the Chase.

Illustrated with 27 full-page and 87 text drawings in half-tone by Howard V. Brown. Cloth, square 12mo, 197 pages; 45 cents. For the intermediate grades.

HERE is portrayed the influence of man's presence upon wild animals. Man's fear, which with the conquest of fire gave way to courage, has resulted in his mastery of many mechanical appliances and in the development of social coöperation, which so increases his power as to make him an object of fear to the wild animals. Since the wild animals now try to escape from man's presence, there is a greater demand made upon man's ingenuity than ever before in supplying his daily food. The way in which man's cunning finds expression in traps, pitfalls, and in throwing devices, and finally in a remarkable manifestation of art, is made evident in these pages.

Book IV. THE EARLY SEA PEOPLE. First Steps in the Conquest of the Waters.

Illustrated with 21 full-page and 110 text drawings in half-tone by Howard V. Brown and Kyohei Inukai. Cloth, square 12mo, 224 pages; 50 cents. For the intermediate grades.

THE life of fishing people upon the seashore presents a pleasing contrast to the life of the hunters on the wooded hills depicted in the previous volumes. The resources of the natural environment; the early steps in the evolution of the various modes of catching fish, of manufacturing fishing tackle, boats, and other necessary appliances; the invention of devices for capturing birds; the domestication of the dog and the consequent changes in methods of hunting; and the social coöperation involved in manufacturing and in expeditions on the deep seas, are subjects included in this volume.

Other volumes, dealing with the early development of pastoral and agricultural life, the age of metals, travel, trade, and transportation, will follow.